Updating Your Old Steam Heating System Using Modern Components

by
Joe Mower

BURD STREET PRESS
SHIPPENSBURG, PENNSYLVANIA

This Burd Street Press publication
was printed by
Beidel Printing House, Inc.
63 West Burd Street
Shippensburg, PA 17257-0708 USA

The acid-free paper used in this book meets the guidelines for permanence and durability of the Committee on Production Guidelines for Book Longevity of the Council on Library Resources.

For a complete list of available publications
please write
Burd Street Press
Division of White Mane Publishing Company, Inc.
P.O. Box 708
Shippensburg, PA 17257-0708 USA

Library of Congress Cataloging-in-Publication Data

Mower, Joe, 1938-
   Updating your old steam heating system using modern components / by Joe Mower.
      p. cm.
   ISBN 1-57249-339-9 (alk. paper)
   1. Dwellings--Heating and ventilation. 2. Steam-heating. I. Title.

TH7467.M68 2003
697'.5--dc21

2003043723

PRINTED IN THE UNITED STATES OF AMERICA

Contents

Preface

Steam heating systems were widely installed in residential and commercial buildings from the late 1800s until the 1940s. Steam heating systems provided an efficient central heat source without the need for electricity to operate pumps or fans. These systems can be easily updated and will continue to provide excellent heating for many years.

Many various types of steam heating systems were installed. All systems fall into two basic classifications. One-pipe systems where the same pipe carries steam to the radiators and returns condensate to the boiler. Two-pipe systems that were installed later had one pipe to carry steam to the radiator and a separate pipe to return the condensate to the boiler. Within each of these two classifications are vapor systems, vacuum systems, gravity return systems, pumped return systems, and mechanical lift systems.

At the time most of these systems were installed the buildings did not have a dependable source of electricity or running water available. The advantage of steam heating systems was they allowed a central heating system without the need for electricity. Many of these systems depend on gravity to return the condensate to the boiler. The old boilers were large and had an adequate reserve of water in the boiler to allow the system to fill with steam during system start-up. The large boiler could also store the returned condensate at the end of the heating cycle.

Due to design changes in modern steam boilers, the methods of firing the boiler and availability of some original

components, these systems need to be updated when the old boiler is replaced with a modern boiler. With the selection of proper components and proper maintenance the old steam system will continue to provide an excellent source of comfort heating.

The old steam boilers were often fired using wood or coal. Many of the systems used special vents, return traps, supply valves, and other piping arrangements to make use of the residual heat in the bed of hot coals. When wood- or coal-fired boilers are converted to gas or oil fired some of these components need to be changed.

The steam boiler itself has been revised, often requiring a system redesign. Old boilers were physically much larger with more available usable water content. When these old boilers are replaced with a smaller modern boiler, consideration must be given to the available water storage. Many times when the boiler is replaced with a physically smaller boiler flooding problems occur, causing poor heating and costly service callbacks.

This book is laid out by type of system in what is often referred to as cookbook style. Each chapter refers to a specific type of installation and is complete to make it easy to follow for the specific type of system you are updating.

This book covers the most popular one-pipe and two-pipe systems. Other types of systems not shown may be similar to one of the systems shown. You can use a similar system as a reference.

Chapter 1

One-Pipe Gravity Return Steam Heating System

The oldest steam heating systems were one-pipe design. The systems had a common pipe to deliver steam from the boiler to the radiators and to return the condensate (condensed steam) back to the boilers. The system piping was pitched to allow the condensate to flow in the bottom of the pipe and the steam could travel freely in the top of the pipe.

Steam promotes its own circulation as it flows naturally from the higher boiler pressure to the system and toward the open vents. The natural flow of steam does not require pumps or fans as with other types of heating systems. On some systems the condensate returns to the boiler by gravity while on other systems a pump may be used to return the condensate.

Automatic air vents were installed on each radiator and also at the end of the steam main to allow air to vent out, as the system filled with steam. The same vent would also allow the air to reenter the system when the steam flow stopped and the steam in the system condensed. Some radiator vents have an adjustable vent port. This allowed the air-venting rate to be adjusted, thus helping to balancing the heat in each room. A smaller vent opening delayed the entry of steam, reducing the heat output; a larger opening allowed steam to enter faster and that radiator would heat faster for more heat.

1

The end of main air vents have a much larger opening to quickly vent air from the heating mains, thus getting heat to all radiators as quick as possible. One important note here is that the end of main vent should be installed at least 15 inches ahead of any elbows and at least 6 inches above the top of the main. This is to prevent condensate from getting into the vent housing and spitting out the vent port. All vents must be installed at least 18 inches above the highest possible boiler water level to keep condensate out of the vent shell.

Steam vents all have a maximum operating pressure rating, which is normally shown on the vent housing. When the boiler operating pressure exceeds the vent rated operating pressure they will close off and remain closed until the system pressure drops below the vent rated pressure. When the vent closes no additional air venting occurs and the air remaining in the system may cause poor heating.

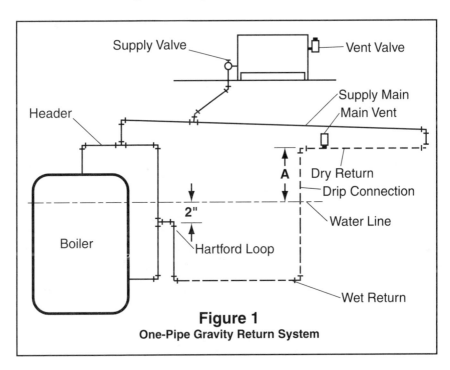

Figure 1
One-Pipe Gravity Return System

The schematic in figure 1 shows the basic piping and components of a one-pipe gravity return system. Steam, being lighter than air, rises from the boiler and flows upward to the supply main and steam radiator. As the steam enters the piping, air must be vented out to allow space for the steam. The boiler header is designed to allow any condensate that may be carried with the steam to flow back into the bottom or the boiler.

The pitch in the steam piping allows the condensate to flow in the bottom of the steam main back to the boiler. In the steam main the condensate flows in the same direction as the steam. This is referred to as parallel flow. In the steam risers from the steam main to the radiation the condensate flows in the opposite direction to the steam. This is referred to as counterflow.

Steam boilers were normally fired at low pressure. This may have been only a few ounces but normally less than 2 psig. The "A" dimension shown in the illustration built up enough static pressure to offset the pressure drop in the steam main due to the steam condensing, friction loss in the piping, and a safety factor to push the condensate back into the boiler.

A common problem in gravity return systems is the boiler pressure is too high and the static head is not enough to push the condensate back to the boiler, thus condensate backs up into the return main and causes water hammer and spitting vents.

When updating a one-pipe gravity system with a new boiler, consideration should be given to installing a boiler feed pump unit. When a boiler feed pump unit is installed, a boiler water level controller is also installed on the boiler to control the pump and to maintain the optimum boiler water level. The boiler feed receiver becomes the surge chamber for the system instead of the new smaller boiler.

An automatic water feeder installed on the boiler feed receiver adds make-up water as needed. The new boiler should also be equipped with a low water burned cut-off and alarm to meet local code requirements.

If a boiler feed pump unit is not installed, the smaller boiler is likely to add make-up water to satisfy the water level requirement during system start-up. This additional water may flood the boiler at the end of the heating cycle, as the steam in the system condenses and returns to the boiler.

Boilers under 30,000 BTU output may not need a boiler feed unit but may require a time delay type automatic boiler feeder to prevent flooding the system. The time delay water feeder cuts off the burner and waits a predetermined amount of time for returns to come back to the boiler. After the predetermined time it will add make-up water, and then the burner will come on and the heating cycle resumes.

The system piping should be inspected to make sure it is properly pitched to allow condensate to drain back to the boiler feed receiver. The steam radiators should pitch slightly toward the supply valve to prevent condensate from holding up in the radiator.

The supply valves should be the type designed for a one-pipe steam system. Do not use a standard gate or globe valve or you will hold up condensate, which may cause water hammer to occur in the radiators. The radiator supply valves on a one-pipe steam system must be fully open to allow proper condensate drainage and prevent water hammer from occurring.

The piping diagram in figure 2 shows the converted one-pipe system with a new boiler feed unit and end of main F&T (float and thermostatic) trap added to the system.

When a boiler feed unit is added an end of main F&T trap must also be added at the end of the steam main. Without

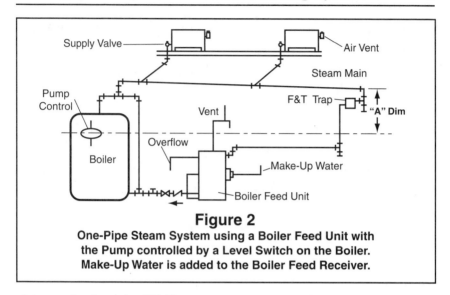

Figure 2
**One-Pipe Steam System using a Boiler Feed Unit with
the Pump controlled by a Level Switch on the Boiler.
Make-Up Water is added to the Boiler Feed Receiver.**

this end of main F&T trap steam will blow directly from
the steam main into the boiler feed receiver and out the
open vent of the boiler feed receiver. The trap should be
installed at least 12 inches below the bottom of the steam
main. This will provide ¼ psig static head at the trap inlet.
The F&T trap should be sized for the full boiler capacity at
¼ psig differential pressure. A safety factor of 2 to 3 times
is also normally added to the trap capacity to allow for higher
condensing during a cold start of the system. The old end of
main air vent may be removed. The thermostatic element
in the F&T trap will allow air to vent from the main into
the vented boiler feed receiver.

The boiler feed receiver should be sized to have 10 to 20
minutes reserve water capacity. Compact two-story buildings normally have a faster return rate than a single-story
building. Large systems will have a longer lag time than a
smaller compact system. The boiler feed unit has an overflow, so if it cannot store all the system returns they will
simply overflow to the drain. Make-up water as required is
added to the boiler feed receiver and pumped into the boiler.
The boiler has a level control to operate the boiler feed pump.

A low water cut-off on the boiler cuts off the burner on low water.

The boiler feed pump discharge piping to the boiler should include a check valve, plug cock or balance valve, and a shut-off valve. When the system is running under normal conditions the plug cock should be throttled until the pressure gauge at the pump discharge is reading the pump discharge pressure shown on the unit nameplate. This reduces the pump required NPSH and helps prevent the pump from cavitating; it also reduces the motor load and prevents short cycling of the pump.

Chapter 2

One-Pipe Pumped Return System

The one-pipe pumped return system is similar to the one-pipe gravity return system, except a condensate pump is used to return the condensate back to the boiler. The condensate pump was installed on systems where sufficient static head was not available to push the condensate back into the boiler or where a higher boiler operating pressure was used. A condensate pump is a unit with a level switch mounted on the unit receiver to start and stop the pump. The receiver is small, so the condensate is quickly returned back into the boiler; it normally has about 1 minute system net storage.

The older large steam boiler had sufficient storage water for the system lag time. The lag time is referred to as the time from where the boiler begins to produce steam until condensate starts to return at an equal rate. During this start-up time the water level in the boiler drops.

The one-pipe design systems had a common pipe to deliver steam to the radiators and to return the condensate (condensed steam) back to the condensate return pump receiver. The system piping was pitched to allow the condensate to flow in the bottom of the pipe and the steam or air could travel freely in the top of the pipe.

Automatic air vents were installed on each radiator to allow air to vent out as the system filled with steam. A F&T trap installed at the end of the main has a thermostatic

element to vented air out of the steam main to the vented condensate receiver; the float element allowed condensate to flow into the condensate receiver. The same vents also allowed the air to reenter the system when the steam flow stopped and the steam in the system condensed. Some radiator vents have an adjustable vent port. This allowed the air-venting rate to be adjusted, thus helping to balance the heat in each room.

Steam vents all have a maximum operating pressure rating, which is normally shown on the vent housing. When the boiler operating pressure exceeds the vent rated operating pressure the steam vents will close off and remain closed until the system pressure drops to the vent rated pressure. When the vent closes no additional air venting occurs and the air remaining in the system causes poor heating.

One important note here is that the end of the main F&T trap should be installed at least 12 inches below the bottom of the steam main. The 12 inches static head will

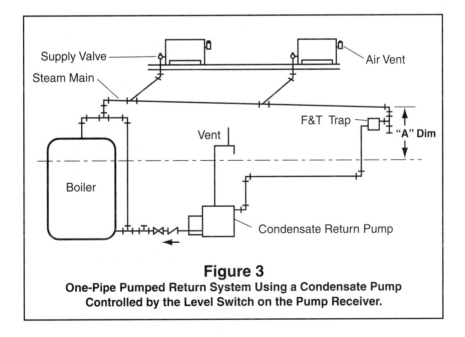

Figure 3
One-Pipe Pumped Return System Using a Condensate Pump
Controlled by the Level Switch on the Pump Receiver.

develop ¼ psig static pressure at the trap inlet. The F&T trap is sized to drain the total boiler load plus a safety factor of at least 2 times.

The schematic in figure 3 shows the basic piping and system components of a one-pipe pumped return system. Steam, being lighter than air, rises from the boiler and upward to the steam main and radiator. As the steam enters the system, air must be vented out to allow space for the steam. The pitch in the steam piping allows the condensate to flow in the bottom of the steam main to the F&T trap.

When updating a one-pipe pumped system with a new boiler, consideration should be given to installing a boiler feed pump unit to replace the condensate transfer unit. With a boiler feed pump unit a boiler water level controller is installed on the boiler to maintain the optimum boiler water level. The boiler feed receiver becomes the surge chamber for the system instead of the new smaller boiler. The automatic water feeder adds water to the boiler feed receiver as needed. The new boiler should also be equipped with a low water burned cut-off to meet local code requirements. Boilers under 30,000 BTU output may not need a boiler feed unit but may require a time delay type automatic boiler feeder to prevent flooding the system. The time delay water feeder cuts off the burner and waits a predetermined amount of time for returns to come back to the boiler. After the predetermined time it will add make-up water and then the burner will come on and the heating cycle resumes.

If the inlet to the boiler feed unit is too high to permit gravity drainage, the old condensate unit can be retained to pump the condensate to the boiler feed receiver inlet. The return piping should not be flooded with condensate, or air will not vent from the system, resulting in poor heat distribution.

If a boiler feed pump unit is not installed the smaller boiler is likely to add make-up water to satisfy the water level requirement during system start-up. This additional water may flood the boiler at the end of the heating cycle, as the steam in the system condenses and returns to the boiler.

The system piping should be inspected to make sure all the piping is properly pitched to allow condensate to drain back to the receiver. The steam radiators should pitch slightly toward the supply valve to prevent condensate from holding up in the radiator. The supply valves should be the type designed for a one-pipe steam system. Do not use a standard gate or globe valve or you will hold up condensate, which will cause water hammer to occur in the radiators.

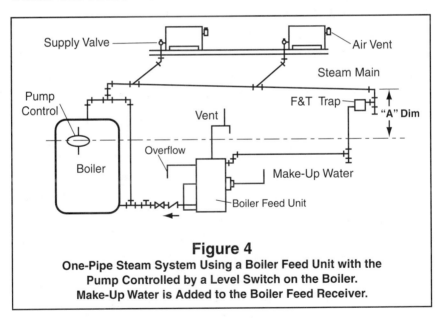

Figure 4
One-Pipe Steam System Using a Boiler Feed Unit with the
Pump Controlled by a Level Switch on the Boiler.
Make-Up Water is Added to the Boiler Feed Receiver.

Figure 4 shows the converted one-pipe system replacing the condensate transfer pump unit with a new boiler feed unit.

The boiler feed receiver should be sized to have 10 to 20 minutes reserve water capacity. Compact two-story buildings

normally have a faster return rate than a single-story building. Large systems will have a longer lag time than smaller compact systems. The boiler feed unit has an overflow so if it cannot store all the system returns they will simply overflow to the drain. Make-up water as required is added to the boiler feed receiver and pumped into the boiler. The boiler has a level control to operate the boiler feed pump. A low water cut-off on the boiler cuts off the burner on low water.

The boiler feed discharge piping to the boiler should include a check valve, plug cock or balance valve, and a shut-off valve. When the system is running under normal conditions the plug cock should be throttled until the pressure gauge at the pump discharge is reading the pump discharge pressure shown on the unit nameplate. This reduces the pump required NPSH and helps prevent the pump from cavitating; it also reduces the motor load and prevents short cycling of the pump.

Chapter 3

One-Pipe Steam Heating System with Mechanical Boiler Return Trap

The use of a boiler return trap was another method used to return condensate to a low-pressure boiler. This method was primarily used where a reliable source of electricity was not available to operate a motor driven condensate transfer pump.

Operation of the unit is a follows. Condensate return by gravity to the boiler return trap housing. When the condensate reached a high level a float mechanism closes off the vent port and opens a steam inlet port. Steam enters the chamber and equalizes with the boiler pressure and condensate flows into the boiler by gravity. A series of check valves in the return piping directs the condensate discharge to the boiler and prevents condensate from flowing back into the return line. The boiler return trap must be installed at least 7 inches above the boiler water line to allow gravity flow. This is shown in the diagram as the "B" dimension.

The receiver vent is simply a chamber with baffle plates used to mount an air vent. The receiver vent is at least 17 inches above the boiler return line. The "A" dimension, which is the differential from the F&T trap inlet to the boiler water line, must be at least 19 inches.

When the boiler was at very low pressure, condensate discharge from the F&T trap could flow directly to the boiler through the check valves. When the boiler pressure was too

high for gravity return the boiler return trap would operate to return the condensate to the boiler.

The systems had one pipe to deliver steam to the radiators and to return the condensate (condensed steam) to the F&T trap. The piping was pitched to allow the condensate to remain in the bottom of the pipe and the steam could flow freely in the top of the pipe.

Automatic air vents were installed on each radiator to allow air to vent out as the system filled with steam. A F&T trap was installed at the end of the main. The thermostatic element in the F&T trap vented air out of the steam main to the receiver vent, and the float element allowed condensate to flow into the vented boiler return trap. The same vents also allowed the air to reenter the system when the steam flow stopped and the steam in the system condensed. Some radiator vents have an adjustable vent port. This allowed the air-venting rate to be adjusted, thus helping to balance the heat in each room.

Steam vents all have a maximum operating pressure rating, which is normally shown on the vent housing. When the boiler operating pressure exceeds the vent rated operating pressure the steam vents will close off and remain closed until the system pressure drops to the vent rated pressure. When the vent closes no additional air venting occurs and the air remaining in the system causes poor heating.

One important note here is that the end of main F&T trap should be installed at least 12 inches below the bottom of the steam main. The 12-inch static head will develop ¼ psig static pressure at the trap inlet. The F&T trap is sized to drain the total boiler load plus a safety factor of 2 to 3 times the actual design capacity. The F&T trap discharge must be at least 19 inches above the boiler water line to return condensate to the boiler return trap. This requires that the bottom of the steam main be at least 31 inches above the boiler water line.

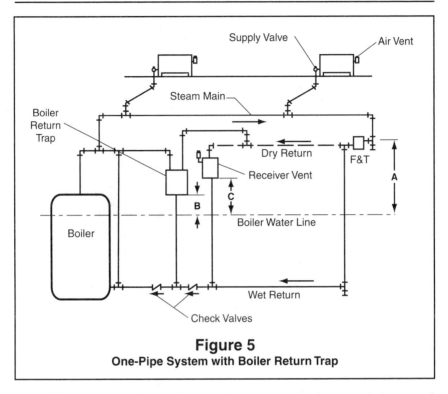

Figure 5
One-Pipe System with Boiler Return Trap

The schematic in figure 5 shows the basic piping and components of a one-pipe boiler return trap system. Steam, being lighter than air, rises from the boiler and upward to the supply main and radiators. As the steam enters the piping, air must be vented out to allow room for the steam. The pitch in the piping allows the condensate to flow in the bottom of the steam main to the F&T trap inlet.

When updating a one-pipe boiler return trap system with a new steam boiler, consideration should be given to installing a boiler feed unit. With a boiler feed unit a boiler water level controller is installed on the boiler to maintain the optimum boiler water level. The boiler feed receiver becomes the surge chamber for the system instead of the new smaller boiler. The need for the old boiler return trap is completely eliminated. An automatic water feeder adds water to the boiler feed receiver as required. The new boiler

should also be equipped with a low water burned cut-off to meet all local code requirements.

If a boiler feed pump unit is not installed, the new smaller boiler is likely to add make-up water to satisfy the water level requirement during system start-up. This additional water may flood the boiler at the end of the heating cycle, as the steam in the system condenses and returns to the boiler. The flooded boiler will cause poor heating and water hammer in the system.

Boilers under 30,000 BTU output may not need a boiler feed unit but may require a time delay type automatic boiler feeder to prevent flooding the system. The time delay water feeder cuts off the burner and waits a predetermined amount of time for returns to come back to the boiler. After the predetermined time it will add make-up water and then the burner will come on and the heating cycle resumes.

Inspect the entire system to make sure all the piping is properly pitched to allow condensate to drain back to the receiver. The steam radiators should pitch slightly toward the supply valve to prevent condensate from holding up in the radiator. The supply valves should be the type designed for a one-pipe steam system. Do not use a standard gate or globe valve or you will hold up condensate, which will cause water hammer to occur in the radiators.

Figure 6 shows the converted boiler return trap system using a new boiler feed unit. If the inlet to the boiler feed unit is too high to allow condensate to flow into the new boiler feed unit, a condensate transfer unit having a lower inlet may be used to pump the condensate into the boiler feed receiver. Condensate must be allowed to flow by gravity for proper air venting and to prevent water hammer.

The boiler feed receiver should be sized to have 10 to 20 minutes reserve water capacity. Compact two-story buildings

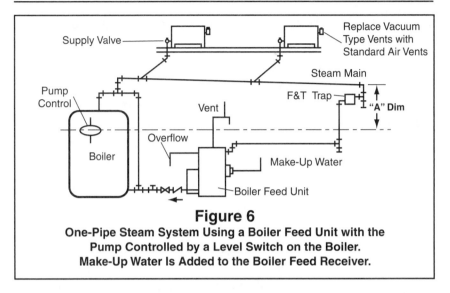

Figure 6
One-Pipe Steam System Using a Boiler Feed Unit with the
Pump Controlled by a Level Switch on the Boiler.
Make-Up Water Is Added to the Boiler Feed Receiver.

normally have a faster return rate than a single-story building. Large systems will have a longer lag time than smaller
compact systems. The boiler feed unit receiver has an overflow, so if it cannot store all the system returns they will
simply overflow to the drain. Make-up water as required is
added to the boiler feed receiver and pumped into the boiler.
The boiler has a level control to operate the boiler feed pump.
A low water cut-off on the boiler cuts off the burner on low
water.

The boiler feed pump discharge piping to the boiler
should include a check valve, plug cock or balance valve,
and a shut-off valve. When the system is running under
normal conditions the plug cock should be throttled until
the pressure gauge at the pump discharge is reading the
pump discharge pressure shown on the unit nameplate. This
reduces the pump required NPSH and helps prevent the
pump from cavitating; it also reduces the motor load and
prevents short cycling of the pump.

Chapter 4

One-Pipe Vapor Steam Heating System

The one-pipe vapor steam heating system was piped the same as a standard one-pipe gravity system. The major differences in the two systems were the type of vents used on the radiators and return line. The vapor system used what was referred to as a vacuum vent. The vacuum vents were constructed to allow air to vent out of the system during start-up, but prevent the reentry of air at the end of the heating cycle, as the system cooled.

The vapor systems were designed for wood- or coal-fired boilers. By preventing the reentry of air, the system would develop an induced vacuum at the end of the heating cycle, as steam in the system condensed. Steam could be generated at less than 212°F under vacuum. Actually these systems often developed about 24" Hg. vacuum allowing steam to be generated as the boiler cooled to about 140°F. This feature allowed more heat to be produced from a ton of coal or a cord of wood by using the residual heat in the hot bed of coals.

Where old steam boilers are converted from coal- or wood-fired, to gas- or oil-fired, the old vacuum vents should be removed and replaced with standard air vents. When vacuum vents are used on a gas- or oil-fired system, they will develop a high-induced vacuum very quickly. This induced vacuum can hold up condensate in the system and may cause water hammer and poor heating. Holding up the

condensate in the system may also cause the boiler to add unnecessary make-up water.

The one-pipe vapor vacuum systems had one pipe to deliver steam to the radiators and return the condensate (condensed steam) back to the boilers. The piping was pitched to allow the condensate to remain in the bottom of the pipe, and the steam could flow freely in the top of the pipe.

An automatic vacuum air vent was installed on each radiator and also the end of the main to allow air to vent out as the system filled with steam. The vent prevented air from reentering the system when the steam flow stopped and the steam in the system condensed.

The end of main vacuum vents have a much larger opening to quickly vent air from the heating mains, thus getting heat to all radiators as quickly as possible. One important note here is that the end of the main vent should be installed at least 15 inches ahead of any elbows and at least 6 inches above the top of the main. This is to prevent condensate from getting into the vent housing and spitting out the vent port. All vents must be installed at least 18 inches above the highest possible boiler water level.

Steam vents all have a maximum operating pressure rating, which is normally shown on the vent housing. When the boiler operating pressure exceeds the vent rated operating pressure they will close off and remain closed until the system pressure drops to the vent rated pressure. When the vent closes, no additional air venting occurs and the air remaining in the system causes poor heating.

The schematic in figure 7 shows the basic piping and components of a one-pipe gravity return system. Steam, being lighter than air, rises from the boiler and upward to the supply main and radiator. As the steam enters, air must be vented out to allow the steam to enter. The boiler header allows any condensate that is carried with the steam to flow

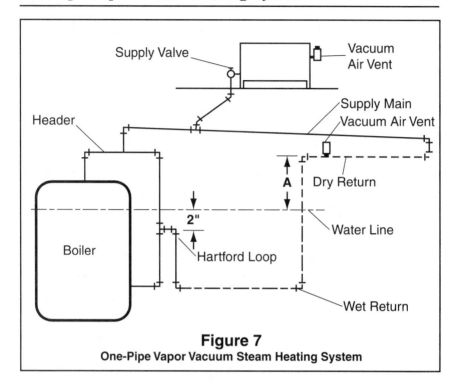

Figure 7
One-Pipe Vapor Vacuum Steam Heating System

back into the bottom of the boiler. The pitch in the piping allows the condensate to flow in the bottom of the steam main back to the boiler. The boiler was normally fired at just a couple of ounces of pressure. The "A" dimension shown in the illustration built up enough static pressure to offset the boiler pressure and push the condensate back into the boiler. A common problem is, if the boiler pressure is too high, the static head is not enough to push the condensate back to the boiler, thus condensate backs up into the return main and causes water hammer and spitting vents.

When updating a one-pipe vapor type gravity system with a new boiler, consideration should be given to installing a boiler feed pump unit. With a boiler feed pump unit a boiler water level controller is installed on the boiler to maintain the optimum boiler water level. The boiler feed receiver becomes the surge chamber for the system instead

of the new smaller boiler. The automatic water feeder adds water to the boiler feed receiver as needed. The new boiler should also be equipped with a low water burned cut-off to meet all local code requirements.

Boilers under 30,000 BTU output may not need a boiler feed unit but may require a time delay type automatic boiler feeder to prevent flooding the system. The time delay water feeder cuts off the burner and waits a predetermined amount of time for returns to come back to the boiler. After the predetermined time it will add make-up water and then the burner will come on and the heating cycle resumes.

If a boiler feed pump unit is not installed, the smaller new boiler is likely to add make-up water to satisfy the water level requirement during system start-up. This additional water may flood the boiler at the end of the heating cycle, as the steam in the system condenses and returns to the boiler.

Inspect the system piping to make sure all system piping is properly pitched to allow condensate to drain back to the receiver. The steam radiators should pitch slightly toward the supply valve to prevent condensate from holding up in the radiator. The supply valves should be the type designed for a one-pipe steam system. Do not use a standard gate or globe valve or you will hold up condensate, which will cause water hammer to occur in the radiators.

Figure 8 shows the converted one pipe vapor system with a boiler feed unit and end of main trap added to the system. The new system is fully vented to prevent any induced vacuum.

When a boiler feed unit is added, an end of main F&T (float and thermostatic) trap must also be added at the end of the main. Without this end of main trap steam will blow directly out the vent of the boiler feed receiver. The trap should be installed at least 12 inches below the bottom of

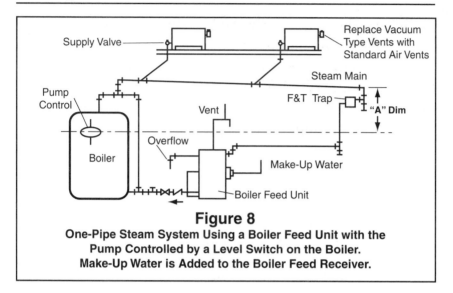

Figure 8
One-Pipe Steam System Using a Boiler Feed Unit with the
Pump Controlled by a Level Switch on the Boiler.
Make-Up Water is Added to the Boiler Feed Receiver.

the steam main. This will provide ¼ psig static head at the trap inlet. The F&T trap should be sized for the full boiler capacity at ¼ psig differential pressure. A 2 to 3 times rated load safety factor is also normally added to the trap capacity to allow for higher condensing during a cold start of the system. The old end of main air vent may be removed. The thermostatic element in the F&T trap will allow air to vent from the main into the vented boiler feed receiver.

The boiler feed receiver should be sized to have 10 to 20 minutes reserve water capacity. Compact two-story buildings normally have a faster return rate than a single-story building. A large system will have a longer lag time than a small compact system. The boiler feed unit has an overflow so if it cannot store all the system returns they will simply overflow to the drain. Make-up water as required is added to the boiler feed receiver and pumped into the boiler. The boiler has a level control to operate the boiler feed pump. A low water cut-off on the boiler cuts off the burner on low water.

The boiler feed discharge piping to the boiler should include a check valve, plug cock or balance valve, and a shut-off valve. When the system is running under normal

conditions the plug cock should be throttled until the pressure gauge at the pump discharge is reading the pump discharge pressure shown on the unit nameplate. This reduces the pump required NPSH and helps prevent the pump from cavitating; it also reduces the motor load and prevents short cycling of the pump.

Chapter 5

One-Pipe Gravity Return System with a Wet Return Line

The oldest steam heating systems were one-pipe design. The systems had a common pipe to deliver steam to the radiators and to return the condensate (condensed steam) back to the boilers. The system piping was pitched to allow the condensate to flow in the bottom of the pipe, and the steam could travel freely in the top of the pipe. The wet return line on this type system drops below the boiler water line and is always filled with condensate. All air venting must occur at the end of the steam main above the boiler water line.

Automatic air vents were installed on each radiator and also at the end of the main to allow air to vent out, as the system filled with steam. The same vent would also allow the air to reenter the system when the steam flow stopped and the steam in the system condensed. Some radiator vents have an adjustable vent port. This allowed the air-venting rate to be adjusted, thus helping to balance the heat in each room.

The end of main air vents have a much larger opening to quickly vent air from the heating mains, thus getting heat to all radiators as quickly as possible. One important note here is that the end of main vent should be installed at least 15 inches ahead of any elbows and at least 6 inches

above the top of the main. This is to prevent condensate from getting into the vent housing and spitting out the vent port. All vents must be installed at least 18 inches above the highest possible boiler water level.

Steam vents all have a maximum operating pressure rating, which is normally shown on the vent housing. When the boiler operating pressure exceeds the vent rated operating pressure, the steam units will close off and remain closed until the system pressure drops to the vent rated pressure. When the vent closes no additional air venting occurs and the air remaining in the system causes poor heating.

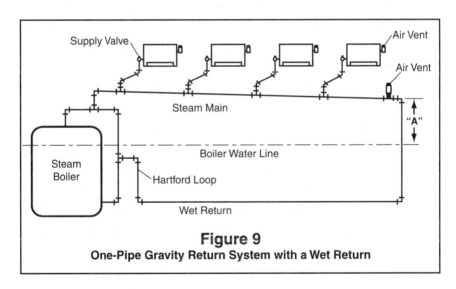

Figure 9
One-Pipe Gravity Return System with a Wet Return

The schematic above shows the basic piping and components of a one-pipe gravity return system with a wet return. Steam, being lighter than air, rises from the boiler and upward to the supply main and radiator. As the steam enters, the piping air must be vented out to allow room for the steam. The boiler header allows any condensate that is carried with the steam to flow back into the bottom of the boiler. The pitch in the piping allows the condensate to flow in the bottom of the steam main back to the boiler.

Steam boilers were normally fired at low pressure. This may have been only a few ounces but normally less than 2 psig. The "A" dimension shown in figure 9 built up enough static pressure to offset the pressure drop in the steam main due to the steam condensing, friction loss in the piping, and a safety factor to push the condensate back into the boiler.

A common problem is if the boiler pressure is too high the static head is not enough to push the condensate back to the boiler, thus condensate backs up into the return main and causes water hammer and spitting vents. (A static head of 27 inches will develop 1 psig pressure.)

When updating any one-pipe gravity system with a new boiler, consideration should be given to installing a boiler feed pump unit. When using a boiler feed pump unit, a boiler water level controller is installed on the boiler to control the pump and to maintain the optimum boiler water level. The boiler feed receiver becomes the surge chamber for the system instead of the new smaller boiler. An automatic water feeder installed on the boiler feed receiver will add water as needed. The new boiler should also be equipped with a low water burned cut-off and alarm to meet local code requirements.

Boilers under 30,000 BTU output may not need a boiler feed unit but may require a time delay type automatic boiler feeder to prevent flooding the system. The time delay water feeder cuts off the burner and waits a predetermined amount of time for returns to come back to the boiler. After the predetermined time it will add make-up water, and then the burner will come on and the heating cycle resumes.

If a boiler feed pump unit is not installed the smaller boiler is likely to add make-up water to satisfy the water level requirement during system start-up. This additional water may flood the boiler at the end of the heating cycle,

as the steam in the system condenses and returns to the boiler.

Inspect the system piping to make sure it is properly pitched to allow condensate to drain back to the boiler feed receiver. The steam radiators should pitch slightly toward the supply valve to prevent condensate from holding up in the radiator. The supply valves should be the type designed for a one-pipe steam system. Do not use a standard gate or globe valve or you will hold up condensate, which will cause water hammer to occur in the radiators. The radiator supply valves on a one-pipe steam system must be fully open to allow proper condensate drainage and prevent water hammer from occurring.

Figure 10 shows the converted one-pipe wet return system with a boiler feed unit and end of main F&T trap added to the system. This system must retain the old end of main air vent, as air cannot vent through the F&T (float and thermostatic) trap and wet return line.

When a boiler feed unit is added, an end of main F&T trap must also be added at the end of the main. Without

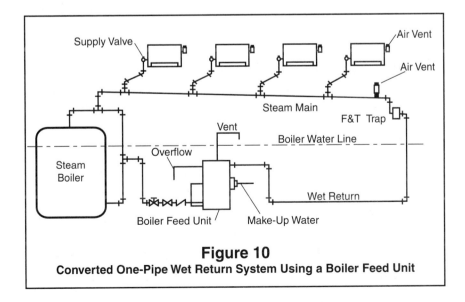

Figure 10
Converted One-Pipe Wet Return System Using a Boiler Feed Unit

this end of main F&T trap steam will blow condensate out of the wet return line and out the vent of the boiler feed receiver. The trap should be installed at least 12 inches below the bottom of the steam main. This will provide ¼ psig static head at the trap inlet. The F&T trap should be sized for the full boiler capacity at ¼ psig differential pressure. A 2 to 3 times safety factor is also normally added to the trap capacity to allow for higher condensing during a cold start of the system. The old end of main air vent must be retained to vent air from the steam main. The thermostatic element in the F&T trap will not allow air to vent from the main through a wet return line.

The boiler feed receiver should be sized to have 10 to 20 minutes reserve water capacity. Compact two-story buildings normally have a faster return rate than a single-story building. Large systems will have a longer lag time than a smaller compact system. The boiler feed unit has an overflow so if it cannot store all the system returns they will simply overflow to the drain. Make-up water as required is added to the boiler feed receiver and pumped into the boiler. The boiler has a level control to operate the boiler feed pump. A low water cut-off on the boiler cuts off the burner on low water.

The boiler feed discharge piping to the boiler should include a check valve, plug cock or balance valve, and a shut-off valve. When the system is running under normal conditions the plug cock should be throttled until the pressure gauge at the pump discharge is reading the pump discharge pressure shown on the unit nameplate. This reduces the pump required NPSH and helps prevent the pump from cavitating; it also reduces the motor load and prevents short cycling of the pump.

Chapter 6

One-Pipe Up-Feed Steam Heating System

An up-feed one-pipe system was used on buildings with more than one floor. Steam was distributed from a basement main to up-feed risers to the upper floors. The condensate flowed down the risers into a wet return line and back to the boiler by gravity. The system piping was pitched to allow the condensate to flow in the bottom of the pipe, and the steam could travel freely in the top of the pipe. The wet return line on this type system drops below the boiler water line and is always filled with condensate. All air venting must occur above the boiler water line.

Automatic air vents were installed on each radiator and also at the end of the main to allow air to vent out as the system filled with steam. The same vent would also allow the air to reenter the system when the steam flow stopped and the steam in the system condensed. Some radiator vents have an adjustable vent port. This allowed the air-venting rate to be adjusted, thus helping to balance the heat in each room.

End of main air vents have a much larger opening to quickly vent air from the heating mains, thus getting heat to all radiators as quickly as possible. One important note here is that the end of main vent should be installed at least 15 inches ahead of any elbows and at least 6 inches above the top of the main. This is to prevent condensate from getting into the vent housing and spitting out the vent port.

All vents must be installed at least 18 inches above the highest possible boiler water level.

Steam vents all have a maximum operating pressure rating, which is normally shown on the vent housing. When the boiler operating pressure exceeds the vent rated operating pressure they will close off and remain closed until the system pressure drops to the vent rated pressure. When the vent closes, no additional air venting occurs and the air remaining in the system causes poor heating.

The schematic in figure 11 shows the basic piping and components of a one-pipe up-feed gravity return system with a wet return. Steam being lighter than air rises from the boiler and upward to the supply main, up-feed risers, and radiators. As the steam enters, the piping air must be vented out to allow room for the steam. The boiler header allows any condensate that is carried with the steam to flow back into the bottom of the boiler. The pitch in the piping allows

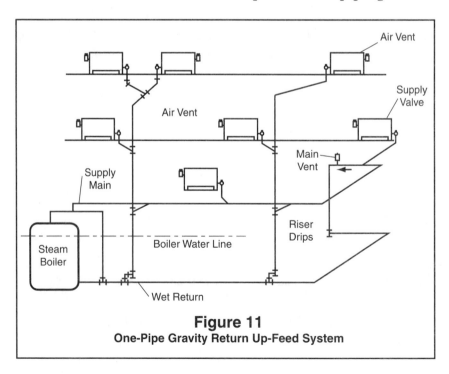

Figure 11
One-Pipe Gravity Return Up-Feed System

the condensate to flow in the bottom of the steam main back to the boiler.

Steam boilers were normally fired at low pressure. This may have been only a few ounces but normally less than 2 psig. The "A" dimension shown in figure 11 built up enough static pressure to offset the pressure drop in the steam main due to the steam condensing, friction loss in the piping, and a safety factor to push the condensate back into the boiler.

A common problem is if the boiler pressure is too high the static head is not enough to push the condensate back to the boiler, thus condensate backs up into the return main and causes water hammer and spitting vents. (A static head of 27 inches will develop 1 psig pressure.)

When updating any one-pipe gravity system with a new boiler, consideration should be given to installing a boiler feed pump unit. When using a boiler feed pump unit, a boiler water level controller is installed on the boiler to control the pump and to maintain the optimum boiler water level. The boiler feed receiver becomes the surge chamber for the system instead of the new smaller boiler. An automatic water feeder installed on the boiler feed receiver will add water as needed. The new boiler should also be equipped with a low water burned cut-off and alarm to meet local code requirements.

Boilers under 30,000 BTU output may not need a boiler feed unit but may require a time delay type automatic boiler feeder to prevent flooding the system. The time delay water feeder cuts off the burner and waits a predetermined amount of time for returns to come back to the boiler. After the predetermined time it will add make-up water, and then the burner will come on and the heating cycle resumes.

If a boiler feed pump unit is not installed the smaller boiler is likely to add make-up water to satisfy the water

level requirement during system start-up. This additional water may flood the boiler at the end of the heating cycle as the steam in the system condenses and returns to the boiler.

Inspect the system piping to make sure it is properly pitched to allow condensate to drain back to the boiler feed receiver. The steam radiators should pitch slightly toward the supply valve to prevent condensate from holding up in the radiator. The supply valves should be the type designed for a one-pipe steam system. Do not use a standard gate or globe valve or you will hold up condensate, which will cause water hammer to occur in the radiators. The radiator supply valves on a one-pipe steam system must be fully open to allow proper condensate drainage and prevent water hammer from occurring.

Figure 12 shows the converted one-pipe up-feed wet return system with a boiler feed unit and F&T (float and thermostatic) traps added to each of the up-feed risers. The F&T traps are sized based on the radiation connected to the individual up-feed riser. This system must retain the old end of main air vent, as air cannot vent through the F&T trap and wet return line. If the return line can be repiped as a dry return then the end air vents could be eliminated.

When a boiler feed unit is added, an end of main F&T trap must also be added at the end of the main. Without this end of main trap steam will blow directly out the vent of the boiler feed receiver. The trap should be installed at least 12 inches below the bottom of the steam main. This will provide one ¼ psig static head at the trap inlet. The F&T trap should be sized for the full boiler capacity at ¼ psig differential pressure. A 2 to 3 times safety factor is also normally added to the trap capacity to allow for higher condensing during a cold start of the system.

The boiler feed receiver should be sized to have 10 to 20 minutes reserve water capacity. Compact two-story

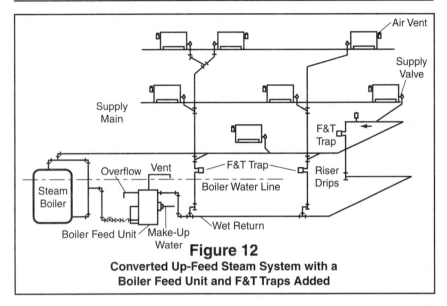

Figure 12
Converted Up-Feed Steam System with a
Boiler Feed Unit and F&T Traps Added

buildings normally have a faster return rate than a single-story building. Large systems will also have a longer lag time than a smaller compact building. The boiler feed unit has an overflow so if it cannot store all the system returns they will simply overflow to the drain. Make-up water as required is added to the boiler feed receiver and pumped into the boiler. The boiler has a level control to operate the boiler feed pump. A low water cut-off on the boiler cuts off the burner on low water.

The boiler feed discharge piping to the boiler should include a check valve, plug cock or balance valve, and a shut-off valve. When the system is running under normal conditions the plug cock should be throttled until the pressure gauge at the pump discharge is reading the pump discharge pressure shown on the unit nameplate. This reduces the pump required NPSH and helps prevent the pump from cavitating; it also reduces the motor load and prevents short cycling of the pump.

Chapter 7

One-Pipe Down-Feed Steam Heating System

The one-pipe down-feed steam heating system has the steam main at the highest point in the system and steam flows down the risers to the lower floors. The steam and condensate flow in the same direction; this is referred to as a one-pipe parallel flow system. The systems had a common pipe to deliver steam to the radiators and to return the condensate (condensed steam) back to the boilers. The system piping was pitched to allow the condensate to flow in the bottom of the pipe and the steam could travel freely in the top of the pipe. The wet return line on this type system drops below the boiler water line and is always filled with condensate. All air venting must occur above the boiler water line.

Automatic air vents were installed on each radiator and also at the end of the main to allow air to vent out as the system filled with steam. Air vents were often installed on the down-feed risers above the boiler water line. The same vents would also allow air to reenter the system when the steam flow stopped and the steam in the system condensed. Some radiator vents have an adjustable vent port. This allowed the air-venting rate to be adjusted, thus helping to balance the heat in each room.

The end of main air vents have a much larger opening to quickly vent air from the heating mains, thus getting heat to all radiators as quickly as possible. One important

note here is that the end of main vent should be installed at least 15 inches ahead of any elbows and at least 6 inches above the top of the main. This is to prevent condensate from getting into the vent housing and spitting out the vent port. All vents must be installed at least 18 inches above the highest possible boiler water level.

Steam vents all have a maximum operating pressure rating, which is normally shown on the vent housing. When the boiler operating pressure exceeds the vent rated operating pressure they will close off and remain closed until the system pressure drops to the vent rated pressure. When the vent closes, no additional air venting occurs and the air remaining in the system causes poor heating.

The schematic in figure 13 shows the basic piping and components of a one-pipe down-feed gravity return system with a wet return. Steam, being lighter than air, rises from the boiler and upward to the supply main and down the

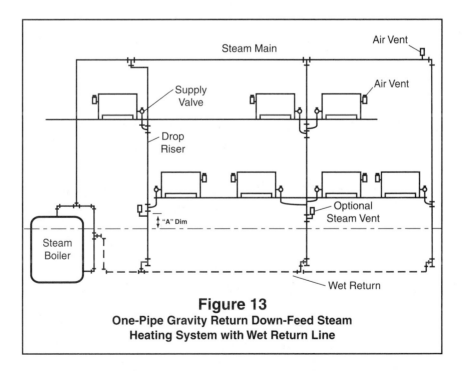

Figure 13
One-Pipe Gravity Return Down-Feed Steam
Heating System with Wet Return Line

risers to the radiators. As the steam enters, the piping air must be vented out to allow room for the steam. The boiler header allows any condensate that is carried with the steam to flow back into the bottom of the boiler. The pitch in the piping allows the condensate to flow in the bottom of the steam main back to the boiler.

Steam boilers were normally fired at low pressure. This may have been only a few ounces but normally less than 2 psig. The "A" dimension shown in figure 13, built up enough static pressure to offset the pressure drop in the steam main due to the steam condensing, friction loss in the piping, and a safety factor to push the condensate back into the boiler.

A common problem is if the boiler pressure is too high the static head is not enough to push the condensate back to the boiler, thus condensate backs up into the return main and causes water hammer and spitting vents. (A static head of 27 inches will develop 1 psig pressure.)

When updating any one-pipe gravity system with a new boiler, consideration should be given to installing a boiler feed pump unit. When using a boiler feed pump unit, a boiler water level controller is installed on the boiler to control the pump and to maintain the optimum boiler water level. The boiler feed receiver becomes the surge chamber for the system instead of the new smaller boiler. An automatic water feeder installed on the boiler feed receiver will add water as needed. The new boiler should also be equipped with a low water burned cut-off and alarm to meet local code requirements.

Boilers under 30,000 Sq. Ft. EDR may not need a boiler feed unit but may require a time delay type automatic boiler feeder to prevent flooding the system. The time delay water feeder cuts off the burner and waits a predetermined amount of time for returns to come back to the boiler.

After the predetermined time it will add make-up water, and then the burner will come on and the heating cycle resumes.

If a boiler feed pump unit is not installed the smaller boiler is likely to add make-up water to satisfy the water level requirement during system start-up. This additional water may flood the boiler at the end of the heating cycle, as the steam in the system condenses and returns to the boiler.

Inspect the system piping to make sure it is properly pitched to allow condensate to drain back to the boiler feed receiver. The steam radiators should pitch slightly toward the supply valve to prevent condensate from holding up in the radiator. The supply valves should be the type designed for a one-pipe steam system. Do not use a standard gate or globe valve or you will hold up condensate, which will cause water hammer to occur in the radiators. The radiator supply valves on a one-pipe steam system must be fully open to allow proper condensate drainage and prevent water hammer from occurring.

Figure 14 shows the converted one-pipe down-feed wet return system with a boiler feed unit and F&T (float and thermostatic) traps added to each down-feed riser. This system must retain the old end of main air vent and down-feed riser vents, as air cannot vent through the F&T trap and wet return line.

When a boiler feed unit is added an end of main F&T trap must also be added at the end of the main. Without this end of main trap steam will blow directly out the vent of the boiler feed receiver. The trap should be installed at least 12 inches below the bottom of the steam main. This will provide ¼ psig static head at the trap inlet. The F&T traps should be sized for the steam load to each trap at ¼ psig differential pressure. A 2 to 3 times safety factor is

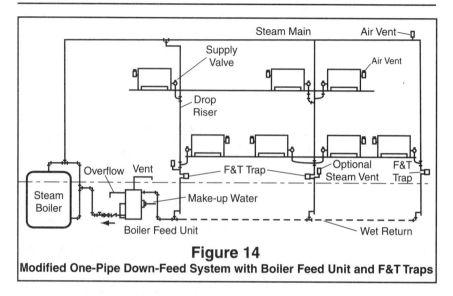

Figure 14

Modified One-Pipe Down-Feed System with Boiler Feed Unit and F&T Traps

also normally added to the trap capacity to allow for higher condensing during a cold start of the system.

The boiler feed receiver should be sized to have 10 to 20 minutes reserve water capacity. Compact two-story buildings normally have a faster return rate than a single-story building. The boiler feed unit has an overflow so if it cannot store all the system returns they will simply overflow to the drain. Make-up water as required is added to the boiler feed receiver and pumped into the boiler. The boiler has a level control to operate the boiler feed pump. A low water cut-off on the boiler cuts off the burner on low water.

The boiler feed discharge piping to the boiler should include a check valve, plug cock or balance valve, and a shut-off valve. When the system is running under normal conditions the plug cock should be throttled until the pressure gauge at the pump discharge is reading the pump discharge pressure shown on the unit nameplate. This reduces the pump required NPSH and helps prevent the pump from cavitating; it also reduces the motor load and prevents short cycling of the pump.

Chapter 8

One-Pipe Air Line Paul Steam Heating System with Vacuum Pump

The one-pipe Air Line Paul steam heating system was a modification made to one-pipe systems for improved heat balance. A standard one-pipe steam system must push the air out of the piping and radiation ahead of the steam at the beginning of each heating cycle. On a large system this may take several minutes before steam gets to the end of the steam main and radiation near the end of the steam main.

To speed up the flow of steam and improve the heat balance a vacuum pump was connected to all the radiation to remove a large portion of the air. This increased the pressure differential across the system and the steam could flow several times faster. This modification was referred to as an Air Line Paul system.

The vacuum pump was connected to each radiator, using copper tubing and a special thermostatic air vent. These vents are manufactured by Hoffman Specialty Company and are referred to as a No. 3 vent.

The vacuum vents allow air to flow to the vacuum pump when the system is cold. When the system filled with steam a thermostatic element inside the vent closed to prevent the passage of steam. The vacuum pump normally operated at 3 to 8 inches Hg. vacuum.

A water jet ejector type vacuum pump can easily handle the air and carryover of steam or water that may occur.

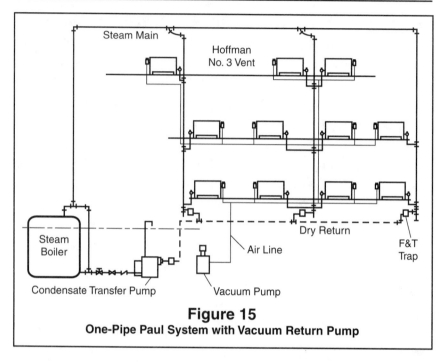

Figure 15
One-Pipe Paul System with Vacuum Return Pump

The schematic in figure 15 shows the basic piping and components of a one-pipe Air Line Paul system with a dry return. Steam, being lighter than air, rises from the boiler upward to the supply main and down the risers to the radiators. As the steam enters the piping, air must be vented out to allow room for the steam.

The vacuum pump pulls air out of the system piping and radiation. The boiler header allows any condensate that is carried with the steam from the boiler to flow back into the bottom or the boiler. The pitch in the piping allows the condensate to flow in the bottom of the steam main back to the condensate transfer pump.

When updating any one-pipe gravity system with a new boiler, consideration should be given to installing a boiler feed pump unit. The vacuum pump should be retained for good heat balance. When using a boiler feed pump unit, a boiler water level controller is installed on the boiler to

control the pump and to maintain the optimum boiler water level. The boiler feed receiver becomes the surge chamber for the system instead of the new smaller boiler. An automatic water feeder installed on the boiler feed receiver will add water as needed. The new boiler should also be equipped with a low water burned cut-off and alarm to meet local code requirements.

Boilers under 30,000 BTU output may not need a boiler feed unit but may require a time delay type automatic boiler feeder to prevent flooding the system. The time delay water feeder cuts off the burner and waits a predetermined amount of time for returns to come back to the boiler. After the predetermined time it will add make-up water, and then the burner will come on and the heating cycle resumes.

If a boiler feed pump unit is not installed the smaller boiler is likely to add make-up water to satisfy the water level requirement during system start-up. This additional water may flood the boiler at the end of the heating cycle, as the steam in the system condenses and returns to the boiler.

Inspect the system piping to make sure it is properly pitched to allow condensate to drain back to the boiler feed receiver. The steam radiators should pitch slightly toward the supply valve to prevent condensate from holding up in the radiator. The supply valves should be the type designed for a one-pipe steam system. Do not use a standard gate or globe valve or you will hold up condensate, which will cause water hammer to occur in the radiators. The radiator supply valves on a one-pipe steam system must be fully open to allow proper condensate drainage and prevent water hammer from occurring.

Figure 16 shows the converted one-pipe down-feed Air Line Paul system. The Paul system can also be applied to an up-feed system and systems with wet returns.

WHITE MANE PUBLISHING CO. INC.

P.O. BOX 708
SHIPPENSBURG PA 17257

Name: _____

Address: _____

Phone: _____

Email: _____
Please PRINT Clearly or Place Address Label Above

Reading Interest

- [ ] History in General
- [ ] Black History
- [ ] Civil War
- [ ] WWI
- [ ] WWII
- [ ] Childrens

- [ ] Guidebook
- [ ] Trivia
- [ ] Military Rosters
- [ ] Army
- [ ] Air Force
- [ ] Coast Guard

- [ ] Marine
- [ ] Naval
- [ ] Unit History
- [ ] Religious
- [ ] Self-Help
- [ ] Other _____

Where Did You Purchase?

- [ ] Online Store
- [ ] Retail Store
- [ ] Direct from Publisher
- [ ] Other _____

Preferred Method of Contact

- [ ] Mail
- [ ] Email
- [ ] Phone
- [ ] Fax _____

- [ ] Yes, please add me to your contact list to receive updated

53399

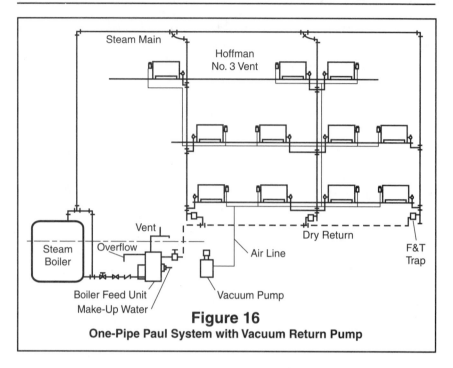

Figure 16
One-Pipe Paul System with Vacuum Return Pump

The boiler feed receiver should be sized to have 10 to 20 minutes reserve water capacity. Compact two-story buildings normally have a faster return rate than a single-story building. Large systems will have a longer lag time than a small compact system. The boiler feed unit has an overflow so if it can not store all the system returns they will simply overflow to the drain.

Make-up water as required is added to the boiler feed receiver and pumped into the boiler. The boiler has a level control to operate the boiler feed pump. A low water cut-off on the boiler cuts off the burner on low water.

The boiler feed discharge piping to the boiler should include a check valve, plug cock or balance valve, and a shut-off valve. When the system is running under normal conditions the plug cock should be throttled until the pressure gauge at the pump discharge is reading the pump discharge pressure shown on the unit nameplate. This reduces

the pump required NPSH and helps prevent the pump from cavitating; it also reduces the motor load and prevents short cycling of the pump.

Chapter 9

Two-Pipe Gravity Return Steam Heating System

The first eight chapters of this manual showed various one-pipe steam heating systems. The one-pipe system had a common pipe to carry both the steam and condensate. Later steam systems were improved with a two-pipe design. The two-pipe design has one pipe to deliver steam to the radiation and a separate pipe to return the condensate to the boiler.

The major advantage of the two-pipe system was the ability to throttle the steam flow into the radiator to balance the heat in individual rooms. Many of the supply valves used in two-pipe systems had a pointer and markings to indicate the valve position. Thermostatically controlled supply valves are also available to control the temperature at each radiator.

The two-pipe system also used smaller pipes, making installation easier. On a two-pipe system, steam enters the radiators at one end near the top. A thermostatic steam trap vents air and drains condensate from the bottom at the opposite end. As the air is heavier than steam the air is completely removed from the radiation.

The two-pipe gravity return system provided a central heating system that could function without the use of electricity. On a two-pipe system the return line is isolated from the steam pressure by steam traps. The only

available pressure to return the condensate to the boiler is the static head built up in the return line; the boiler operating pressure for a gravity return system is just a few ounces. If the boiler pressure is too high, condensate will back up into the return line and cause poor heating and water hammer.

The old two-pipe steam systems can be updated to continue to provide excellent comfort heating.

The schematic in figure 17 shows the basic two-pipe gravity return system. The operating cycle is as follows.

When the boiler is fired the water is heated to boiling temperature. As additional heat is added, steam rises from the water surface into the boiler header to the steam main and to the radiation. Air in the steam main is vented through the thermostatic element in the F&T trap into the dry return. Air in the radiation is vented through the

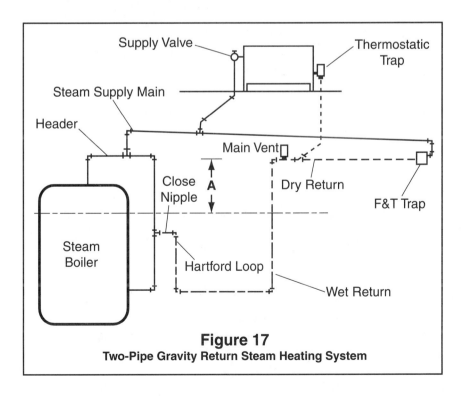

Figure 17
Two-Pipe Gravity Return Steam Heating System

thermostatic traps on each radiator into the dry return. A main air vent located on the dry return vents the air from the dry return. As steam in the main condenses it flows by gravity to the F&T trap, and the float mechanism inside the trap allows it to drain to the dry return. The steam condensed in the radiators is drained through the thermostatic trap into the dry return.

The thermostatic traps close when the condensate is near saturation temperature. The thermostatic element in the F&T traps closes when it is near saturation temperature. The float element in the F&T trap closes when the condensate is drained. Live steam is kept out of the dry return line by the steam traps.

As condensate backs up into the wet return line it develops a static pressure to push the condensate into the boiler. Most of the systems were designed for an 18-inch minimum static head between the boiler water level and the end of the dry return. The 18-inch static head develops about ½ psig pressure. The static pressure built up in the wet return must be higher than the boiler operating pressure. Most steam boilers in a two-pipe gravity return system operated at less than 6 ounces pressure.

The end of main air vent must be located on a dry return to prevent spitting. The vent should be installed at least 15 inches ahead of any elbows and 6 to 10 inches above the dry return line. The steam vent should only see air or steam; condensate must be kept out of the vent to prevent spitting of condensate.

When updating a two-pipe gravity system with a new boiler, consideration should be given to installing a boiler feed pump unit. When using a boiler feed pump unit, a boiler water level controller is installed on the boiler to control the pump and to maintain the optimum boiler water level. The boiler feed receiver becomes the surge chamber for the

system instead of the new smaller boiler. An automatic water feeder installed on the boiler feed receiver will add water as needed. The new boiler should also be equipped with a low water burned cut-off and alarm to meet local code requirements.

If a boiler feed pump unit is not installed, the smaller boiler is likely to add make-up water to satisfy the water level requirement during system start-up. This additional water may flood the boiler at the end of the heating cycle as the steam in the system condenses and returns to the boiler.

Boilers under 30,000 BTU output may not need a boiler feed unit but may require a time delay type automatic boiler feeder to prevent flooding the system. The time delay water feeder cuts off the burner and waits a predetermined amount of time for returns to come back to the boiler. After the predetermined time it will add make-up water, and then the burner will come on and the heating cycle resumes.

The system piping should be inspected to make sure it is properly pitched to allow condensate to drain back to the boiler feed receiver.

The following piping diagram shows the converted two-pipe system with a boiler feed unit added to the system.

The old end of main air vent may be removed. The thermostatic element in the F&T trap will allow air to vent from the main into the vented boiler feed receiver.

The boiler feed receiver should be sized to have 10 to 20 minutes reserve water capacity. Compact two-story buildings normally have a faster return rate than a single-story building. A large system will also have a longer lag time than a small compact system.

The boiler feed unit has an overflow so if it cannot store all the system returns they will simply overflow to a drain. Make-up water as required is added to the boiler feed receiver and pumped into the boiler. The boiler has a

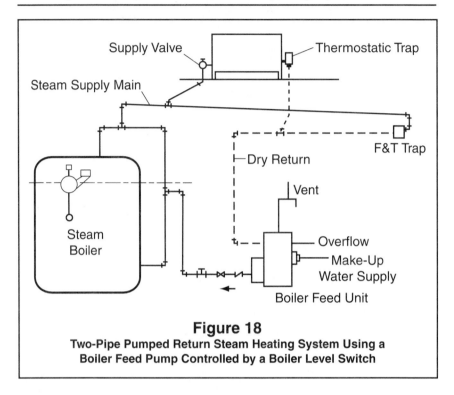

Figure 18
Two-Pipe Pumped Return Steam Heating System Using a
Boiler Feed Pump Controlled by a Boiler Level Switch

level control to operate the boiler feed pump. A low water cut-off on the boiler cuts off the burner on low water.

The boiler feed discharge piping to the boiler should include a check valve, plug cock or balance valve, and a shut-off valve. When the system is running under normal conditions the plug cock should be throttled until the pressure gauge at the pump discharge is reading the pump discharge pressure shown on the unit nameplate. This reduces the pump required NPSH and helps prevent the pump from cavitating; it also reduces the motor load and prevents short cycling of the pump.

Chapter 10

Two-Pipe Pumped Return System

The major advantage of the two-pipe system was the ability to throttle the steam flow into the radiator to balance the heat in individual rooms. Many of the supply valves used in two-pipe systems had a pointer and markings to indicate the valve position. Thermostatically controlled supply valves are also available to control the temperature at each radiator.

The two-pipe system also used smaller pipes, making installation easier. On a two-pipe system, steam enters the radiators at one end near the top, and condensate is drained through a thermostatic steam trap near the bottom at the other end.

The two-pipe pumped return system provided a central heating system with a condensate return pump to return the condensate to the boiler. With a pump to return the condensate, the boiler could operate at a higher pressure than a gravity return system. The return line is isolated from the steam pressure by the steam traps. The old two-pipe steam systems can be updated to continue to provide excellent comfort heating.

The schematic in figure 19 shows the basic two-pipe pumped return system using a condensate pump controlled by a level switch on the pump receiver. The operating cycle is as follows.

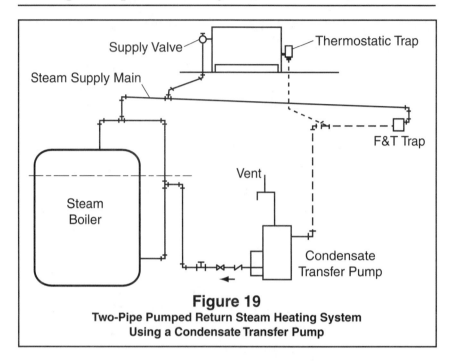

Figure 19
Two-Pipe Pumped Return Steam Heating System
Using a Condensate Transfer Pump

When the boiler is fired, the water is heated to boiling temperature. As additional heat is added, steam rises from the water surface into the boiler header to the steam main and to the radiation. Air in the steam main is vented through the thermostatic element in the F&T trap into the dry return. Air in the radiation is vented through the thermostatic traps on each radiator into the dry return.

The dry return line allows air to flow to the vented condensate receiver vent line. As steam in the main condenses it flows by gravity to the F&T trap and the float mechanism allows it to drain to the dry return. The steam condensed in the radiators is drained through the thermostatic trap into the dry return.

The thermostatic traps close when the condensate is near saturation temperature. The thermostatic element in the F&T traps closes when it is near saturation temperature. The float element in the F&T trap closes when the

condensate is drained. Live steam is kept out of the dry return line by the steam traps.

The condensate flows by gravity to the condensate receiver. When the condensate receiver reaches a high level, a float switch starts the pump and returns the condensate to the boiler.

When updating a two-pipe pumped return system using a condensate transfer pump with a new boiler, consideration should be given to installing a boiler feed pump unit. When using a boiler feed pump unit, a boiler water level controller is installed on the boiler to control the pump and to maintain the optimum boiler water level.

The boiler feed receiver becomes the surge chamber for the system instead of the new smaller boiler. If the inlet connection on the new boiler feed unit is too high to allow condensate to flow by gravity, the old condensate transfer unit can be used to pump the condensate to the boiler feed unit inlet. The return line cannot be flooded or air will not vent from the system, resulting in poor heating.

An automatic water feeder installed on the new boiler feed receiver adds water as needed. The new boiler should also be equipped with a low water burned cut-off and alarm to meet local code requirements.

If a boiler feed pump unit is not installed the smaller boiler is likely to add make-up water to satisfy the water level requirement during system start-up. This additional water may flood the boiler at the end of the heating cycle, as the steam in the system condenses and returns to the boiler.

Boilers under 30,000 BTU output may not need a boiler feed unit but may require a time delay type automatic boiler feeder to prevent flooding the system. The time delay water feeder cuts off the burner and waits a predetermined amount of time for returns to come back to the boiler. After the predetermined time it will add make-up water, and then the burner will come on and the heating cycle resumes.

The system piping should be inspected to make sure it is properly pitched to allow condensate to drain back to the boiler feed receiver.

The piping diagram in figure 20 shows the converted two-pipe pumped return system with a boiler feed unit added to the system.

The thermostatic element in the F&T trap will allow air to vent from the main into the vented boiler feed receiver. The F&T trap is sized to drain the condensation in the steam mains, not the entire boiler load as in the one-pipe system.

The boiler feed receiver should be sized to have 10 to 20 minutes reserve water capacity. Compact two-story buildings normally have a faster return rate than a single-story building. A large system will have a longer lag time than a small compact system.

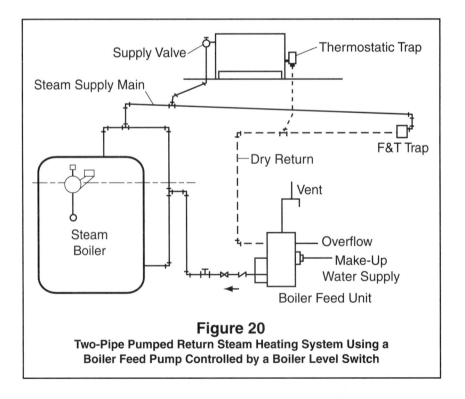

Figure 20
Two-Pipe Pumped Return Steam Heating System Using a Boiler Feed Pump Controlled by a Boiler Level Switch

The boiler feed unit has an overflow so if it cannot store all the system returns they will simply overflow to a drain. Make-up water as required is added to the boiler feed receiver and pumped into the boiler. The boiler has a level control to operate the boiler feed pump. A low water cut-off on the boiler cuts off the burner on low water.

The boiler feed discharge piping to the boiler should include a check valve, plug cock or balance valve, and a shut-off valve. When the system is running under normal conditions the plug cock should be throttled until the pressure gauge at the pump discharge is reading the pump discharge pressure shown on the unit nameplate. This reduces the pump required NPSH and helps prevent the pump from cavitating; it also reduces the motor load and prevents short cycling of the pump.

Chapter 11

Two-Pipe Steam Heating System Using a Boiler Return Trap

The major advantage of the two-pipe system was the ability to throttle the steam flow into the radiator to balance the heat in individual rooms. Many of the supply valves used in two-pipe systems had a pointer and markings to indicate the valve position. Thermostatically controlled supply valves are also available to control the temperature at each radiator.

The two-pipe system also used smaller pipes, making installation easier. On a two-pipe system, steam enters the radiators at one end near the top, and condensate is drained through a steam trap near the bottom at the other end.

With a boiler return trap to return the condensate, the boiler could operate at a higher pressure than a gravity return system. The boiler return trap was used instead of a motor driven condensate transfer pump when a reliable source of electricity was not available. The return line on a two-pipe system is isolated from the steam pressure by the steam traps. The two-pipe steam systems can be updated to continue to provide excellent comfort heating.

The schematic in figure 21 shows the basic two-pipe boiler return trap system. The operating cycle is as follows.

When the boiler is fired the water is heated to the boiling temperature. As additional heat is added steam rises from the water surface into the boiler header to the steam main and to the radiation. Air in the steam main is vented

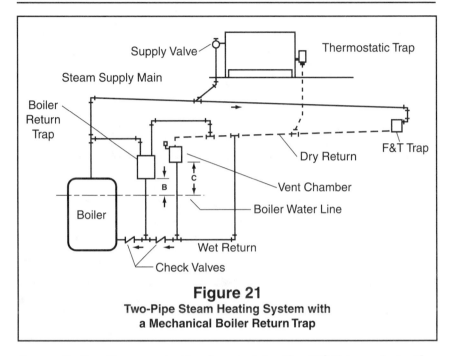

Figure 21
Two-Pipe Steam Heating System with
a Mechanical Boiler Return Trap

through the thermostatic element in the F&T trap into the dry return. Air in the radiation is vented through the thermostatic traps on each radiator into the dry return. The dry return line allows air to flow to the vented chamber and through the steam vent to atmosphere.

As steam in the main condenses it flows by gravity to the F&T trap, and the float mechanism allows it to drain to the dry return. The steam condensed in the radiators is drained through the thermostatic trap into the dry return. Condensate can flow by gravity to the boiler return trap through either the dry return or the wet return line.

When the condensate in the boiler return trap reaches the high level a float mechanism inside the trap closes the vent line and opens the trap body to the boiler pressure. The trap body being higher than the boiler water line allows condensate to flow into the boiler. When the condensate level in the trap body reaches the low level the boiler line is closed and the vent reopens. Condensate from the

system again flows to the boiler return trap body and the cycle is repeated.

The thermostatic traps on the radiators close when the condensate is near saturation temperature. The thermostatic element in the F&T traps closes when it is near saturation temperature. The float element in the F&T trap closes when the condensate is drained. Live steam is kept out of the return line by the steam traps.

When updating a two-pipe boiler return trap system with a new boiler, consideration should be given to installing a boiler feed pump unit. When using a boiler feed pump unit, a boiler water level controller is installed on the boiler to control the pump and to maintain the optimum boiler water level. The boiler feed receiver becomes the surge chamber for the system instead of the new smaller boiler. An automatic water feeder installed on the new boiler feed receiver will add water as needed. The new boiler should also be equipped with a low water burned cut-off and alarm to meet local code requirements.

If a boiler feed pump unit is not installed the smaller boiler is likely to add make-up water to satisfy the water level requirement during system start-up. This additional water may flood the boiler at the end of the heating cycle, as the steam in the system condenses and returns to the boiler.

Boilers under 30,000 BTU output may not need a boiler feed unit but may require a time delay type automatic boiler feeder to prevent flooding the system. The time delay water feeder cuts off the burner and waits a predetermined amount of time for returns to come back to the boiler. After the predetermined time it will add make-up water, and then the burner will come on and the heating cycle resumes.

The system piping should be inspected to make sure it is properly pitched to allow condensate to drain back to the boiler feed receiver, keeping the return line dry.

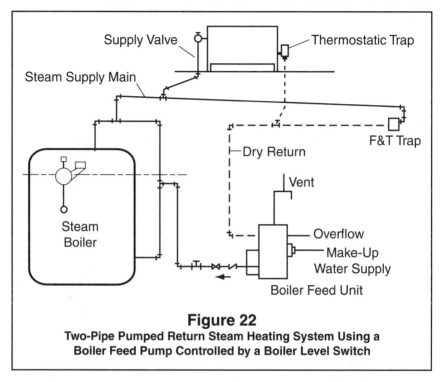

Figure 22
Two-Pipe Pumped Return Steam Heating System Using a
Boiler Feed Pump Controlled by a Boiler Level Switch

Figure 22 shows the converted boiler return trap system with a boiler feed unit added to the system. The old boiler return trap has been eliminated. The thermostatic element in the F&T trap will allow air to vent from the steam main into the vented boiler feed receiver. The F&T trap is sized to drain the condensation in the steam mains, not the entire boiler load as in the one-pipe system.

The boiler feed receiver should be sized to have 10 to 20 minutes reserve water capacity. Compact two-story buildings normally have a faster return rate than a single-story building. A large system will have a longer lag time than a smaller compact system.

The boiler feed unit has an overflow so if it cannot store all the system returns they will simply overflow to a drain. Make-up water as required is added to the boiler feed receiver and pumped into the boiler. The boiler has a level

control to operate the boiler feed pump. A low water cut-off on the boiler cuts off the burner on low water.

The boiler feed discharge piping to the boiler should include a check valve, plug cock or balance valve, and a shut-off valve. When the system is running under normal conditions the plug cock should be throttled until the pressure gauge at the pump discharge is reading the pump discharge pressure shown on the unit nameplate. This reduces the pump required NPSH and helps prevent the pump from cavitating; it also reduces the motor load and prevents short cycling of the pump.

Chapter 12

Two-Pipe Vacuum Return System

The major advantage of the two-pipe system was the ability to throttle the steam flow into the radiator to balance the heat in individual rooms. Many of the supply valves used in two-pipe systems had a pointer and markings to indicate the valve position. Thermostatically controlled supply valves are also available to control the temperature at each radiator.

The two-pipe system also used smaller pipes, making installation easier. On a two-pipe system, steam enters the radiators at one end near the top, and condensate is drained through a steam trap near the bottom at the other end.

Some larger systems used a vacuum return pump to pull a vacuum on the piping system; the same unit often pumped the condensate directly back into the boiler.

The advantage of the vacuum pump was to provide faster steam distribution for better heat balance. The vacuum pump created a vacuum on the return line. When the system was cold the thermostatic traps on the radiators and the thermostatic element in the F&T traps were also open; this allowed the vacuum to be pulled on the radiation and distribution pipes. The vacuum pump normally was set to operate between 3" Hg. and 8" Hg. vacuum. With the system under vacuum, steam could travel much faster to all the radiation for more even heating.

The vacuum pump receiver normally had two compartments. The one compartment where the return line entered was under vacuum. The vacuum chamber had an equalizing line connected to the boiler header with a check valve; this equalizing line prevented the boiler from going under a higher vacuum than the vacuum receiver when the system shut down and steam in the boiler condensed. Without this equalizing line a high vacuum at the boiler could hold up condensate in the system and produce water hammer.

The equalizing line also had a second check valve to allow any positive pressure to vent directly to atmosphere. The check valves were normally a soft-seated type and were located in a seal loop. This seal loop allowed condensate to form at the check valve and prevented the steam temperature from destroying the elastomer in the check valve seat. The second compartment of the vacuum pump was normally vented directly to atmosphere.

The return line is isolated from the steam pressure by the steam traps. The old two-pipe vacuum return steam systems can be updated to continue to provide excellent comfort heating. In most cases the vacuum operation should be retained to provide even heat distribution.

The schematic in figure 23 shows the basic two-pipe vacuum return system. The operating cycle is as follows.

When the boiler is fired the water is heated to the boiling temperature. As additional heat is added steam rises from the water surface into the boiler header to the steam main and to the radiation. The return line and radiation is under vacuum produced by the vacuum return unit. Additional air in the steam main is vented through the thermostatic element in the F&T trap into the dry return. Additional air in the radiation is vented through the thermostatic traps on each radiator into the dry return. The dry return line allows air to flow to the vacuum pump through the vacuum pump vent to atmosphere. As steam in the main

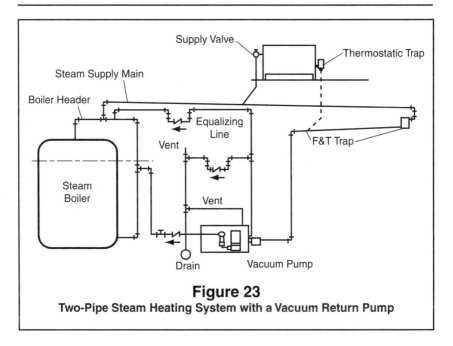

Figure 23
Two-Pipe Steam Heating System with a Vacuum Return Pump

condenses it flows by gravity to the F&T trap, and the float mechanism allows it to drain to the dry return. Steam condensed in the radiators drains through the thermostatic traps into the dry return line. The condensate can then flow by gravity in the dry return line to the vacuum pump inlet. When the condensate level in the vacuum unit reaches the high level a float mechanism inside the receiver starts the pump, and condensate is returned to the boiler. When the condensate in the receiver reaches the low water level the condensate flow is stopped.

The thermostatic traps close when the temperature of the condensate is near saturation temperature. The thermostatic element in the F&T traps closes when it is near saturation temperature. The float element in the F&T trap closes when the condensate is drained. Live steam is kept out of the return line by the steam traps. When the system is at operating temperature, vacuum is just maintained on the return line.

When updating a two-pipe vacuum return system with a new boiler, consideration should be given to installing a boiler feed pump unit. When using a boiler feed pump unit, a boiler water level controller is installed on the boiler to control the pump and to maintain the optimum boiler water level. The boiler feed receiver becomes the surge chamber for the system instead of the new smaller boiler. An automatic water feeder installed on the new boiler feed receiver will add water as needed. The new boiler should also be equipped with a low water burned cut-off and alarm to meet local code requirements.

If a boiler feed pump unit is not installed the smaller boiler is likely to add make-up water to satisfy the water level requirement during system start-up. This additional water may flood the boiler at the end of the heating cycle, as the steam in the system condenses and returns to the boiler.

Boilers under 30,000 BTU output may not need a boiler feed unit but may require a time delay type automatic boiler feeder to prevent flooding the system. The time delay water feeder cuts off the burner and waits a predetermined amount of time for returns to come back to the boiler. After the pre-determined time it will add make-up water, and then the burner will come on and the heating cycle resumes.

The system piping should be inspected to make sure it is properly pitched to allow condensate to drain back to the boiler feed receiver, keeping the return line dry.

In Figure 24 the new boiler feed unit has a cast iron receiver good for vacuum service and a separate vacuum pump. This maintains the condensate under vacuum and is the preferred method of updating the system. If you use a lower cost steel receiver boiler feed unit, not good for vacuum service, and retain the old vacuum condensate transfer unit the system should be piped as shown in figure 24A.

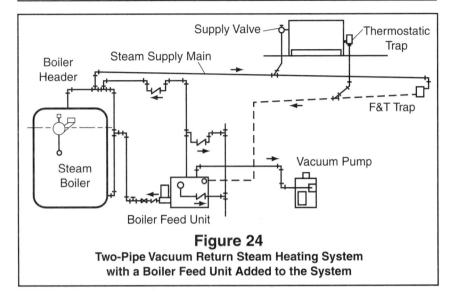

Figure 24
Two-Pipe Vacuum Return Steam Heating System
with a Boiler Feed Unit Added to the System

With a vacuum pump it is very important to maintain the steam traps to prevent the vacuum pumps from cavitating and destroying themselves.

The boiler feed receiver should be sized to have 10 to 20 minutes reserve water capacity. Compact two-story buildings normally have a faster return rate than a single-story building. A large system will have a longer lag time than a smaller system.

The boiler feed unit has an overflow so if it cannot store all the system returns they will simply overflow to a drain. Make-up water as required is added to the boiler feed receiver and pumped into the boiler. The boiler has a level control to operate the boiler feed pump. A low water cut-off on the boiler cuts off the burner on low water.

The boiler feed discharge piping to the boiler should include a check valve, plug cock or balance valve, and a shut-off valve. When the system is running under normal conditions the plug cock should be throttled until the pressure gauge at the pump discharge is reading the pump discharge pressure shown on the unit nameplate. This reduces

the pump required NPSH and helps prevent the pump from cavitating; it also reduces the motor load and prevents short cycling of the pump.

Figure 24A shows the converted two-pipe vacuum return system with a vented boiler feed unit added to the system. The vacuum pump should be maintained to help maintain the heat balance in the system.

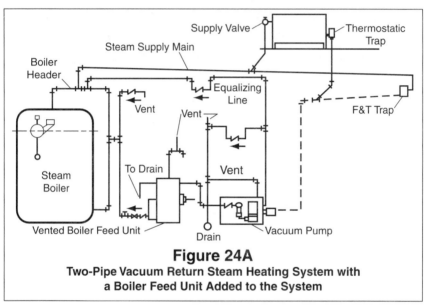

Figure 24A
Two-Pipe Vacuum Return Steam Heating System with a Boiler Feed Unit Added to the System

One of the common problems that occur when using a vented boiler feed receiver is that when the boiler shuts down, an induced vacuum created in the boiler draws water from the vented boiler feed receiver into the boiler and floods the boiler.

There are several ways to deal with this problem. The above diagram shows a check valve installed on the boiler feed discharge line near the boiler open to atmosphere. This allows air to flow into the boiler to break the vacuum instead of drawing water from the boiler feed receiver. This does create another problem in that the vacuum pump will not be able to pull a shut-off vacuum when thermostatic traps open. This problem can be solved by installing an

aquastat on the boiler header wired in series with the vacuum switch. This will shut off the vacuum pump when the boiler is below the steam temperature. This can also be an energy saving device on systems that have a lot of air leaks causing excessive running of the vacuum pumps when the vacuum is not needed.

Another method of preventing the boiler from drawing water from the boiler feed receiver is to install a solenoid valve of motorized valve in the boiler feed pump discharge line. A solenoid valve often closes too fast and causes objectionable noise in the system piping. The motorized valve has a slower opening and closing time and is a better choice.

Chapter 13

Two-Pipe Comfort Heat System with Differential Loop

The two-pipe gravity return Comfort Heat System was a Vapor Steam Heating System designed by Hoffman Specialty Company. The major difference in this system compared to a standard two-pipe gravity return system was the differential loop and vacuum vents. The vacuum vents were constructed to allow air to vent out of the system during start-up, but prevent the reentry of air at the end of the heating cycle, as the system cooled.

The Comfort Heat Systems were designed for wood- or coal-fired boilers. By preventing the reentry of air the system would develop an induced vacuum. Steam could be generated at less than 212°F under vacuum. Actually these systems often developed about 24" Hg. vacuum, allowing steam to be generated as the boiler cooled to about 140°F. This feature allowed more heat to be produced from a ton of coal or a cord of wood from the residual heat in the hot bed of coals.

Where old boilers are converted from coal- or wood-fired, to gas- or oil-fired, the old vacuum vents should be removed and replaced with standard air vents. When vacuum vents are used on a gas- or oil-fired system, a high induced vacuum will develop very quickly. This induced vacuum will hold up condensate in the system and may cause water hammer and poor heating.

The differential loop had no moving parts. The device used a tube inside a water leg to prevent the boiler pressure from exceeding the return line pressure by more than 10 ounces. When the boiler operating pressure exceeded the return line pressure by more than 10 ounces the water seal was uncovered and steam would blow into the return line to equalize the pressures.

The system piping was pitched to allow the condensate to remain in the bottom of the pipe and the steam or air could flow freely in the top of the pipe.

A thermostatic trap was installed on each radiator to vent air and drain condensate. The thermostatic trap prevented live steam from passing into the return line. A thermostatic trap was also installed on the end of the steam main to allow air to vent into the return line as the system filled with steam.

The schematic shows the basic piping and components of the two-pipe gravity return Comfort Heat System. Steam, being lighter than air, rises from the boiler and upward to

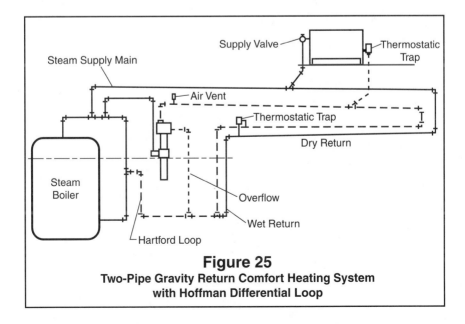

Figure 25
Two-Pipe Gravity Return Comfort Heating System
with Hoffman Differential Loop

the supply main and radiator. As the steam enters the system, air must be vented out to allow room for the steam. The air is vented through the thermostatic traps on the radiators and end of the steam main into the return line and out through the air vent.

The boiler header allows any condensate that is carried with the steam to flow back into the bottom or the boiler. The pitch in the piping allows the condensate to flow in the bottom of the steam main back to the boiler. The boiler was normally fired at just a couple of ounces of pressure. If the boiler pressure is too high, the static head in the return line is not enough to push the condensate back into the boiler. The differential loop seal allowed steam into the return line to prevent condensate from backing up into the return main, causing water hammer and spitting vents.

When updating a Comfort Heat System with a new boiler, consideration should be given to installing a boiler feed pump unit. With a boiler feed pump unit a boiler water level controller is installed on the boiler to maintain the optimum boiler water level. The boiler feed receiver becomes the surge chamber for the system instead of the new smaller boiler. The automatic water feeder adds water to the boiler feed receiver as needed.

The new boiler should also be equipped with a low water burned cut-off to meet all local code requirements.

When adding a boiler feed unit, an end of main F&T trap must be added to prevent live steam from flowing into the vented receiver. The air vent in the F&T trap will vent air from the steam main. Air in the return line can vent directly into the boiler feed receiver, thus the old air vent in the return line can be eliminated. The thermostatic trap at the end of the main can also be removed and the connections plugged.

If a boiler feed pump unit is not installed, the smaller new boiler is likely to add make-up water to satisfy the water

level requirement during system start-up. This additional water may flood the boiler at the end of the heating cycle, as the steam in the system condenses and returns to the boiler.

Boilers under 30,000 BTU output may not need a boiler feed unit but may require a time delay type automatic boiler feeder to prevent flooding the system. The time delay water feeder cuts off the burner and waits a predetermined amount of time for returns to come back to the boiler. After the predetermined time it will add make-up water, and then the burner will come on and the heating cycle resumes.

When a smaller boiler is used to replace the old boiler, and the differential loop is retained, the boiler must be positioned to keep the same boiler water line elevation as the old boiler.

Inspect the system piping to make sure all the system piping is properly pitched to allow condensate to drain back to the receiver. The steam radiators should pitch slightly toward the thermostatic trap to prevent condensate from

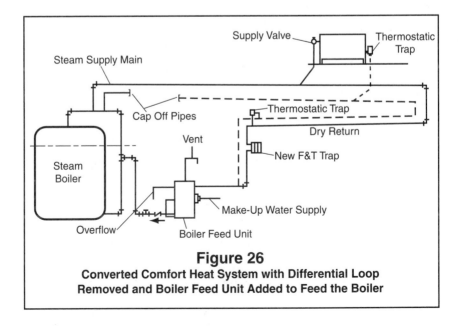

Figure 26
Converted Comfort Heat System with Differential Loop
Removed and Boiler Feed Unit Added to Feed the Boiler

holding up in the radiator. Do not use standard gate or globe valves on the radiators or you will hold up condensate and cause water hammer to occur in the risers.

Figure 26 shows the converted two-pipe Comfort Heat System with a boiler feed unit and end of main trap added to the system. The new system is fully vented to prevent any induced vacuum.

When a boiler feed unit is added an end of main F&T (float and thermostatic) trap must also be added at the end of the main. Without this end of main trap steam will blow directly out the vent of the boiler feed receiver. The trap should be installed at least 12 inches below the bottom of the steam main. This will provide ¼ psig static head at the trap inlet. The F&T trap should be sized for the condensation load of the steam main not the full boiler capacity. A 2 to 3 times actual load safety factor is also normally added to the trap capacity to allow for higher condensing during a cold start of the system. The old end of main air vent and thermostatic trap may be removed.

The boiler feed receiver should be sized to have 10 to 20 minutes reserve water capacity. Compact two-story buildings normally have a faster return rate than a single-story building. A large system will also have a longer lag time than a smaller compact system.

The boiler feed unit has an overflow so if it can not store all the system returns they will simply overflow to the drain. Make-up water as required is added to the boiler feed receiver and pumped into the boiler. The boiler has a level control to operate the boiler feed pump. A low water cut-off on the boiler cuts off the burner on low water.

The boiler feed discharge piping to the boiler should include a check valve, plug cock or balance valve and a shut-off valve. When the system is running under normal conditions the plug cock should be throttled until the pressure

gauge at the pump discharge is reading the pump discharge pressure shown on the unit nameplate. This reduces the pump required NPSH and helps prevent the pump from cavitating; it also reduces the motor load and prevents short cycling of the pump.

Chapter 14

Hot Water Loop off Steam Boiler

Using steam to add heat to a basement room on a steam heating system presents a problem as the radiation is too low to allow gravity return of the condensate. One way to handle this problem is to add a pumped hot water loop to the steam boiler.

Adding a hot water loop to a steam boiler requires special design considerations. A hot water boiler normally

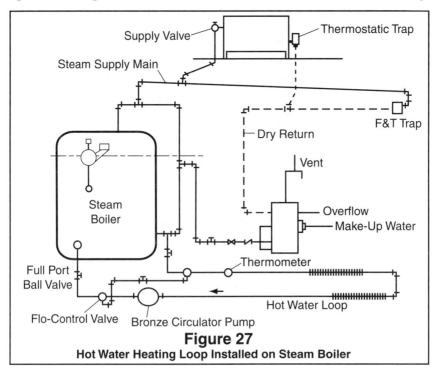

Figure 27
Hot Water Heating Loop Installed on Steam Boiler

operates below 180°F and the hot water boiler is in a closed pressurized loop.

The steam boiler is vented and the water can be at saturation temperature. The open loop is more corrosive than a closed loop, therefore the circulator pump should always be all bronze construction. The water near saturation temperature can cause a circulator pump to cavitate. To prevent the pump from cavitating a hot water bypass loop can be installed. The bypass loop blends the recirculated water from the hot water loop with the boiler water to keep the temperature below 180°F. This will have to be manually adjusted when the system is operating using the Flo-control valves shown in figure 27.

The circulator pump is installed on the return side of the hot water loop so it pumps the lower temperature water.

The boiler control must also be revised to maintain heat in the hot water loop when the boiler is not firing for the steam loop. This can be accomplished by adding a thermostat in the area heated by the hot water loop. The thermostat is wired to start the circulator pump and fire the boiler. An aquastat must be added to the boiler to cut off the burner when the water reaches 160 to 180°F.

Full port ball valves are provided to allow servicing the hot water loop without draining the boiler. If the hot water loop is above the boiler water line hose bibs will be required to manually prime the loop at initial start-up. There should not be any automatic air vents on the hot water loop, or air will enter and break the water seal.

Chapter 15

Vacuum Lifts and Accumulator Tanks

One advantage of return systems that employed the use of a vacuum pump was the ability to lift condensate from low returns. One method of handling low returns was to use a lift fitting. There were commercial lift fittings available or you can make your own as shown in the following illustration.

The purpose of the lift fitting was to completely drain condensate from the low return line before pulling air from the system. The vacuum switch sensing line on the vacuum pump must be connected to a dry return on the system side of the low return line to prevent short cycling of the vacuum pump.

The lift pipe was sized ½ the return line pipe size to provide higher velocity and better lifting. The top of the lift pipe was fitted with a couple of elbows to assure that the condensate flowed toward the vacuum pump and not back down the lift pipe when the vacuum pump shut off.

Another method of lifting low return lines was to use an accumulator tank. The advantage of a accumulator tank was that the float switch on the receiver operated the vacuum pump and kept the return lines completely dry at all times. The vacuum switch sensing line on the vacuum unit must be connected to the accumulator tank to prevent short cycling and to pull a vacuum on the entire system.

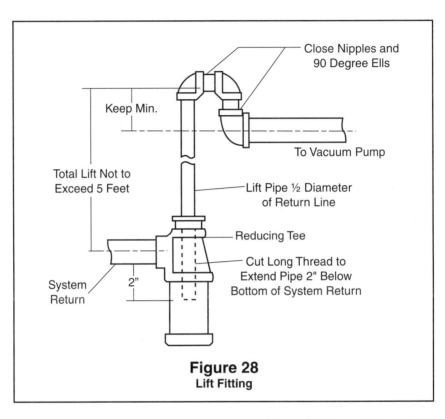

Figure 28
Lift Fitting

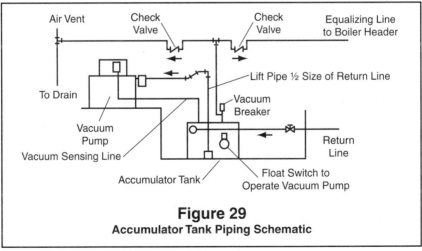

Figure 29
Accumulator Tank Piping Schematic

On systems with either a lift fitting or accumulator the vacuum pump must be retained to assure condensate return. Many of the old vacuum systems have developed leaks in the piping or have steam traps that leak and the vacuum pump operates continuously wasting energy.

The steam traps must be maintained to prevent excessive condensate return temperature. The condensate temperature in a low-pressure steam system should be less than 180°F. The return lines in steam systems should not be insulated to keep the condensate return temperature down to acceptable temperature levels.

Where an accumulator tank is used the vacuum switch can be bypassed, and only the float switch operates the vacuum pump. In some installations where vacuum is only required at start-up for more even heating, an aquastat can be added to the vacuum switch circuit. This will allow the vacuum pump to operate during a cold start and then cut out the vacuum switch when the return condensate gets over 180°F. The float switch on the accumulator tank will start the vacuum pump to transfer condensate.

Where a lift fitting is used without an accumulator tank the vacuum must be maintained at all times unless the system is modified to eliminate the lift fitting. A condensate transfer pump can be installed to eliminate the lift fitting.

Chapter 16

Steam to Water Heat Exchangers

Steam to water heat exchangers are often used to add a hot water heating zone off a steam boiler, or to provide hot water for commercial or domestic use. On a steam to water heat exchanger steam enters the top of the shell and the condensate (condensed steam) is drained from the bottom of the shell through a steam trap. The fluid being heated is circulated through the tube bundle. The cold fluid enters the bottom of the heat exchanger tube bundle and the hot fluid exits at the top.

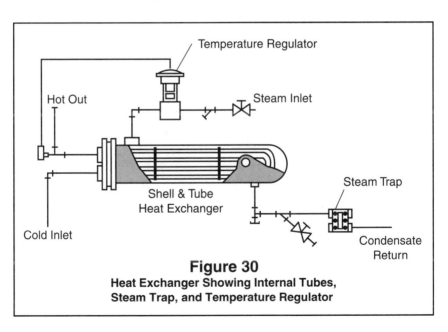

Figure 30
Heat Exchanger Showing Internal Tubes,
Steam Trap, and Temperature Regulator

When the shell and tube heat exchanger is used to heat water for domestic hot water constant circulation should always be provided to obtain better temperature control. Without constant circulation the time delay for a temperature regulator to respond can cause temperature spikes that could cause serious injury. A buffer tank or storage tank to provide system storage will provide even better temperature control.

When selecting a heat exchanger to heat water to temperatures less than 200°F, it should be selected for a maximum internal steam pressure of 2 psig. The low steam pressure has a lower temperature that will help to prevent excessive temperature overshoots. The steam temperature at 2 psig is only 219°F. Low-pressure operation will also allow the use of a low-pressure F&T steam trap that has a larger orifice size and is less costly than a high-pressure F&T steam trap.

The low-pressure steam operation provides lower temperature condensate out of the steam trap and reduces flash steam loss for more efficient operation. It will also allow the use of lower cost standard condensate pumps and eliminate the need for additional condensate coolers.

PROPERTIES OF SATURATED STEAM (APPROX).

Gauge Pressure at Sea Level	Saturation Temperature °F	Heat in Water BTU per Lb.	Latent Heat in Steam BTU
0	212	180	970
2	219	187	966
5	227	195	960
10	240	208	952
15	250	219	945
30	274	243	929
50	281	250	924
70	303	273	908
100	338	309	881
125	353	325	868

The properties of saturated steam table show the relationship of the steam saturation temperature at various steam pressures. The amount of re-evaporation or flash steam is actually twice as much at 5 psig operation as at 2 psig operation. The flash steam at 100 psig operation is 18 times greater than at 2 psig.

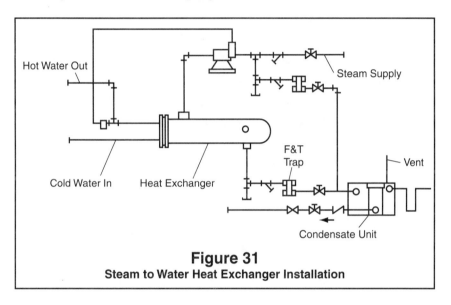

Figure 31
Steam to Water Heat Exchanger Installation

Planning the Heat Exchanger Installation

Locate the heat exchanger for easy access and allow room to remove the tube bundle. The heat exchanger shell should pitch slightly toward the condensate outlet.

Mount the heat exchanger high enough to allow the condensate from the steam trap to drain by gravity to a vented condensate unit.

With a steam heat exchanger it is important to provide complete condensate removal under all operating conditions. When a modulating temperature regulator is used in the steam supply, the internal steam shell pressure can often be 0 psig regardless of the steam supply to the steam regulator. This is particularly true on a new installation where

the heat exchanger fouling factor normally adds about 30% additional tube surface area to allow for corrosion and fouling as the system ages. Until the scale and corrosion builds up on the tubes the heat exchanger is oversized and will operate at a much lower pressure.

The steam trap should be installed 15 inches below the heat exchanger shell. The 15-inch static head will provide $1/2$ psig pressure to the F&T trap inlet. The F&T steam trap is then sized for the heat exchanger maximum condensing load at $1/2$-psi differential pressure plus a safety factor of two times the actual load to allow for start-up conditions.

The steam trap should drain by gravity into a vented condensate transfer unit. Any lift in the condensate return piping must be avoided for good temperature control and to prevent water hammer that can destroy the heat exchanger tubes, steam traps, and steam regulator. A dry return line is also necessary for proper air venting from the heat exchanger shell at start-up.

Any rise in the condensate return line will allow condensate to back up into the heat exchanger shell, causing poor temperature control. Remember that during start-up and during light loads the heat exchanger steam pressure will be 0 psig.

What happens when the condensate can not drain by gravity is that condensate backs up into the heat exchanger shell and the heat exchanger loses tube surface area. The steam regulator then opens allowing more steam pressure to maintain the temperature. As the steam pressure builds, the condensate is pushed out and the entire tube surface is exposed to the hotter steam, causing a temperature overshoot. The regulator then closes and the temperature drops. It takes time for the temperature regulator to respond to the drop in temperature, resulting in wide temperature fluctuations

going out to the system. This situation can be avoided by providing gravity drainage of the condensate.

The temperature regulator should be sized for the actual maximum steam load. Oversizing the temperature regulator will cause poor temperature control. The temperature-sensing bulb must be fully inserted in the hot water outlet piping. A steam strainer should be provided ahead of the regulator, and a "y" type strainer in the steam supply should be located with the dirt pocket to the side to prevent a condensate pocket. A drip trap should be installed in the steam supply ahead of the temperature regulator to assure dry steam to the regulator at all times.

A vacuum breaker is installed on the heat exchanger shell to prevent an induced vacuum from forming in the shell. A vacuum can hold condensate in the heat exchanger shell, resulting in poor temperature control and water hammer. During light loads the condensing of the steam causes an induced vacuum in the shell that will pull air in through the vacuum breaker. The heat exchanger will operate with steam at the top, a layer of air in the center to reduce the amount of tube surface exposed to the steam and condensate in the bottom draining toward the steam trap.

The return line between the heat exchanger and the condensate unit should not be insulated to help cool the condensate temperature to the condensate transfer unit.

The schematic figure 32 shows an installation using a buffer tank to provide domestic hot water. The buffer tank should have approximately 5 minutes storage capacity. The circulator pump provides constant system re-circulation in the system and should be sized to have a minimum flow of 20% of the system maximum draw rate.

The blending of the system return and the cold make up-water smoothes out the temperature going to the heat exchanger, allowing better temperature control.

The illustration in figure 33 shows a large storage tank heated by an external shell and tube heat exchanger. The

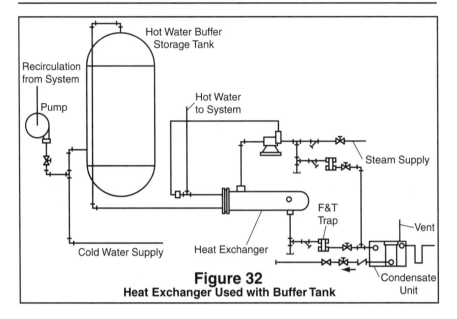

Figure 32
Heat Exchanger Used with Buffer Tank

temperature sensor is located in the storage tank. This type of installation provides the best temperature control.

This method can also be used to replace a damaged tank heater with an external shell and tube heat exchanger.

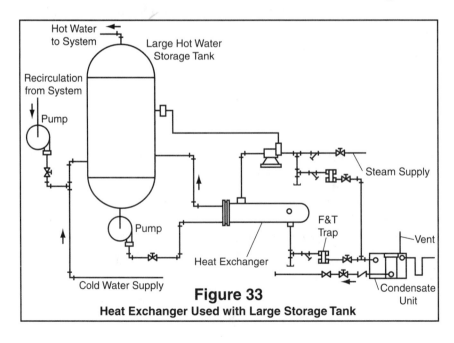

Figure 33
Heat Exchanger Used with Large Storage Tank

Chapter 17

Steam Trap Testing

Properly operating steam traps are important for the efficient operation of a steam heating system. When steam traps fail they allow steam to enter the return line, increasing the condensate temperature and in many cases allow steam to flow from the open vents on condensate and boiler feed receivers.

In a low-pressure steam heating system using thermostatic traps and F&T traps the normal condensate temperature is around 160°F. The return lines were deliberately not insulated to allow the condensate to cool. When steam traps start to blow by, the condensate temperature increases. The centrifugal pumps used on the condensate and boiler feed units can start to cavitate when the condensate temperature starts to increase above the design temperature. The actual temperature they start to cavitate will vary by the pump design but it is often around 180 to 190°F.

A good method of tracking steam trap performance is to install a thermometer on the boiler feed or condensate receiver. When the condensate temperature starts to increase it is time to start testing the steam traps.

To perform a trap survey start with a plot plan showing where the various traps are located. It will help to have someone along who is familiar with the system. Traps are often hidden in crawl spaces and closets and are easy to miss.

Systems with a lot of traps should have the traps identified with a number. Locate the trap on the plot plan and attach a metal tag to the trap to give it permanent identification. On large installations you may want to set up a computer program locating the traps.

Note all information about the trap, including the manufacturer, size, type, model number, orifice size if shown, and application.

Energy lost due to a failed steam trap can be determined with this information. There are several computer programs available to calculate energy loss from failed steam traps.

The recommended list of equipment includes pen or pencil, notebook, flashlight, hardhat, large pliers, hammer, scraper, stepladder, kneepads, digital thermometer, and automotive type stethoscope; an ultrasound device is desirable but due to the cost it may not be justified for small installations.

The steam system must be operating to test the trap operation.

System Problems That Cause Trap Failures

Dirt can plug strainer screens and internal passageways in the trap, or deposit on the trap seat to prevent tight closing.

Dirt can plug the vent hole in the top of the bucket on inverted bucket traps. This will allow air to be trapped in the top of the bucket, closing the trap.

Water hammer is often created by high temperature condensate flashing in a wet return line, causing steam bubbles to form in the condensate. When the steam bubbles implode, the resulting force is referred to as water hammer. The forces created by water hammer can destroy floats and thermostats.

Water hammer can be caused by lifts in the return line
or traps discharging into wet return lines. Check valves
should be installed after traps that have lifts in the return
line or discharge into pressurized return lines. The check
valve isolates the trap from the water hammer.

Cause of Trap Failures

Dirt can plug passageways or deposit on the trap seat
to prevent tight closing. Seats and plugs can become worn
or wiredrawn and prevent tight closing. Linkage joints can
become worn, causing misalignment of the pin and seat.

Water hammer can destroy floats or thermostats.

System Problems

Air venting—air is normally vented from the steam
space by the steam trap into a gravity return line. Traps
that discharge into wet return lines, pressurized return lines,
or have a lift in the return line can cause poor venting. Separate air vents may be required to vent the air to gravity
returns or atmospheric conditions.

Steam Trap Testing

Most trap testing is done by sound using an automotive type stethoscope or an ultrasound device. By listening
to a good trap and then a trap that is passing steam the
difference in sound is easily distinguished. It only takes listening to a few traps to learn when you come to a defective
trap.

A steam trap blowing live steam will make a low pitch
whistle. A steam trap draining condensate will make a wet
gurgling sound.

The most positive method of testing a steam trap is to
see what is passing through the trap. If a test valve is provided on the discharge side of the trap open the valve and

see what it is passing. Remember, you are dealing with hot steam, therefore open gate valves slowly.

Thermostatic Traps

Thermostatic traps use a bellows or diaphragm assembly with a volatile fluid inside. As the fluid inside the element is heated it vaporizes, causing an internal pressure to expand the bellows or diaphragms and close the discharge port. The element will close 10 to 30 degrees below the steam temperature to prevent passage of live steam.

The thermostatic traps can fail either closed or open, depending on the design. Failure can occur due to dirt plugging the discharge port or by loss of the internal fill. When the trap fails closed, the result will be loss of heat in the unit it serves. When the unit fails open, it will pass live steam into the discharge line.

Test using a digital thermometer. The temperature at the trap inlet should be sub cooled 10 to 30°F below the steam temperature ahead of the trap. A cold trap may be an indication that the trap failed closed. Make sure the steam is turned on.

Test using a stethoscope or ultrasound. You should be able to hear the trap cycle. A low-pitch whistle sound indicates a trap blowing live steam.

Inverted Bucket Traps

Inverted bucket traps use an inverted bucket with a small orifice in the top of the bucket. The trap housing inlet passage enters under the bucket; when air or steam enters the bucket faster than it can bleed through the orifice, it collects in the top of the bucket. The buoyancy lifts the bucket and closes the trap. When condensate enters, the weight of the bucket causes it to sink and the trap opens, draining the condensate until it again sees air or steam.

The bucket trap cycles open and shut. You can hear the metallic sound as the bucket sinks and again when the bucket rises closing the seat.

Test trap using test valve. The trap should be draining condensate with some flash steam. A failed open trap will blow live steam. A failed closed trap will be cold. You should be able to see the trap cycle open and shut.

Test using a stethoscope. You should hear a wet gurgling sound as the trap drains condensate. A low-pitch whistle sound indicates a trap blowing live steam. You should be able to hear a metallic sound as the trap opens and shuts.

Test using a digital thermometer. The temperature at the trap inlet should be at or close to the steam temperature ahead of the trap. A cold trap may be an indication that the trap failed closed. Make sure the steam is turned on. The temperature downstream of the trap should drop off as you move away from the trap. Compare temperature readings with other traps in similar applications. A higher temperature indicated the trap is passing live steam.

Float & Thermostatic Traps

The F&T trap has two separate mechanisms. The float mechanism opens and closes a port for draining condensate. The float assembly modulates to drain condensate equal to the system-condensing rate. The thermostatic element is located above the condensate level in the trap. The thermostatic assembly vents air from the system into the return line. The thermostatic element uses a bellows or diaphragm assembly with a volatile fluid inside. As the fluid inside the element is heated it vaporizes, causing an internal pressure to expand the bellows or diaphragms and close the discharge port. The element will close 10 to 30 degrees below the steam temperature to prevent passage of live steam.

To test an F&T trap using test valve on the discharge side of the trap. The trap should be draining condensate with some flash steam. A failed open trap will blow live steam. A failed closed trap will be cold. Flash steam can be distinguished from live steam as it has a grayish color and is a lazy slow velocity. Live steam is clear as it leaves the pipe, and as it starts to condensate you see a grayish color appear, which has a much higher velocity.

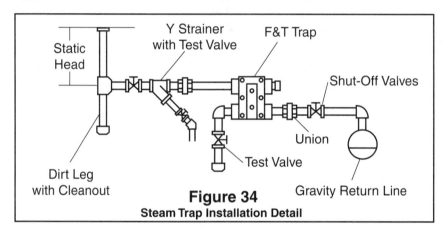

Figure 34
Steam Trap Installation Detail

Test using a stethoscope. You should hear a wet gurgling sound as the trap drains condensate. A low-pitch whistle sound indicates a trap blowing live steam.

Test using a digital thermometer. The temperature at the trap inlet should be at or close to the steam temperature ahead of the trap. A cold trap may be an indication that the trap failed closed. Make sure the steam is turned on. The temperature downstream of the trap should drop off as you move away from the trap. Compare temperature readings with other traps in similar applications.

Thermo Disc Traps

Thermo disc traps use a free-floating disc to open and close the trap. As steam enters the trap it builds up a pressure on top of the disc, closing it against the discharge port.

When the steam on top of the disc condenses it opens, allowing any condensate to drain.

Thermo disc traps should normally only be used when the steam pressure is over 10 psig. At lower pressures the operation becomes sluggish and it starts to waste steam.

Test using a stethoscope or sound measurement. You should hear the trap cycle open and closed. In most installations this can be heard with the naked ear. Normally a disc trap will open every 20 seconds or less. A low-pitch whistle sound indicates the trap is blowing live steam. Rapid cycling (machine gunning) indicates a worn seat, which will waste steam. A cold trap indicates the trap is plugged or failed shut.

Helpful Conversion Factors
for Steam Systems

One Boiler Horsepower = 140 Square Feet EDR, 33,475 Btu per Hour or 34.5 Pounds per Hour steam at 212° F.

1,000 Square Feet EDR Yields 0.5 GPM of Condensate.

1,000 Pounds per Hour Condensate = 2 GPM.

To Convert Sq. Ft. EDR to Lbs. per Hour of Condensate, Divide by 4.

0.25 Lbs./Hr. Condensate = 1 Sq. Ft. EDR.

1 Sq. Ft. EDR (Steam) = 240 Btu/Hr. with 215°F Steam Filling the Radiator and 70°F Air Surrounding the Radiator.

To Convert Btu/Hr. to Lbs./Hr., Divide the Btu/Hr. by 960.

One PSI = 2.307 Feet of Static Head Water (Cold).

One PSI = 2.41 Feet of Static Head Water (Hot at 212°F).

One Inch Mercury = 13.6 Inches Water Column.

One PSI = 2.036 Inches Mercury.

Pump Sizing Factors

Size Condensate and Boiler Feed Pump Capacity at 2 to 3 Times Actual Running Load Capacity.

Add 5 PSI to Required Discharge PSI for Pressures under 50 PSI, add 10 PSI for Required Pressure over 50 PSI.

Size Condensate Receivers for 1 Minute Net Storage Capacity.

Size Boiler Feed Receivers for 10 to 20 Minute Net Storage Capacity.

One Boiler Horsepower Evaporation Rate = 0.069 GPM.

Frequently Asked Questions

Q. What is a Hartford Loop and why is it there?

A. The Hartford Loop is a special piping arrangement in the boiler return connection designed to prevent excessive water from backing out of the boiler. When the boiler water level dropped below the Hartford Loop horizontal pipe connection, steam would blow into the return line; this helped prevent excessive low water in the boiler. The Hartford Loop was normally connected 2 inches below the normal boiler water line.

This piping arrangement was developed by the Hartford Insurance Company to help prevent boiler explosions due to low water. At the time the Hartford Loop was introduced, many boilers were coal- or wood-fired and not equipped with a low water burner cut-off. Many installations also did not have a pressurized water supply and the boiler was not equipped with an automatic water feeder.

Q. Why is the Hartford Loop connected with a close nipple?

A. When the water level in the boiler drops to the Hartford Loop horizontal pipe connection, the pipe may have steam in the top and condensate in the bottom. Turbulence in the water can cause steam pockets to get trapped in the piping connection. By using a close nipple the size of the steam pocket is minimized and the water hammer that occurs when a steam bubble collapses is minimized. Thus the close pipe nipple minimizes water hammer in the piping.

Q. What causes water hammer in a steam system?

A. Water hammer is caused by a steam bubble imploding as it gets trapped in condensate. Water hammer often occurs in a sagging steam pipe or a pipe that is partially filled with condensate such as a wet return line that may be installed too high. It may also occur in a one-pipe steam radiator where the supply valve is not fully open, causing condensate to back up in the radiator. An improperly pitched steam radiator or steam riser can also cause water hammer.

The force caused by a steam pocket imploding can cause pipes to shake violently and sometimes break a pipe connection. This is the same condition that occurs in a pump suction and is referred to as cavitation.

Q. What causes a condensate or boiler feed pump to cavitate?

A. Pump cavitation is caused by steam bubbles forming in the pump suction. A negative pressure is developed as fluid is drawn into the impeller inlet. When the water passes through this negative pressure, steam pockets can form; these steam pockets then implode as they reach a positive pressure in the impeller vanes. The design of the impeller and the fluid temperature determines how much cavitation will occur. In the worst case the pump will become vapor bound and will stop pumping.

Pump cavitation can cause vapor to form around the pump shaft seal, causing them to overheat and fail.

Throttling the pump flow rate, thus reducing the amount of negative pressure created in the impeller suction, can often eliminate cavitation. To throttle the pump flow install a pressure gauge at the pump discharge. Use a plug cock, globe valve or balance valve to throttle the flow until the discharge pressure gauge reads the unit nameplate pressure.

Defective steam traps in the system will increase the condensate temperature. The normal condensate return temperature at the condensate or boiler feed receiver in a steam heating system is normally 160 to 180°F.

Condensate return lines are not normally insulated to help reduce condensate temperature. If the return lines are insulated resulting in higher condensate temperature, special low NPSH pumps may be needed to prevent cavitation.

Q. What is a boiler header?

A. A boiler header is the near boiler piping arrangement designed to prevent condensate carryover from the boiler. All boiler manufactures have a recommended piping arrangement that should be followed closely. The boiler header usually includes a swing joint connection between multiple boiler outlets to help reduce stress on the boiler. The boiler header includes a drip connection to drain any carryover back into the boiler.

The steam main take-off from the boiler header should be located between the last boiler outlet and the drip connection. This keeps the steam and condensate flowing in the same direction for better condensate drainage.

Q. What is a dry return line?

A. A dry return line is a return pipe above the boiler water line and any static head that may occur. Dry return lines carry condensate in the bottom portion of the pipe, and the top of the pipe is free to vent air from the system. A dry return should never be flooded with condensate.

Q. What is a wet return line?

A. A wet return line is a return pipe installed below the boiler water level. Air cannot pass through a wet return line.

Q. What is static head?

A. Static head is pressure developed by a column of water. A 27-inch column of water will develop 1 psig pressure. In a gravity return steam heating system static head is used to offset the boiler operating pressure and push the condensate back into the boiler.

Q. How does a thermostatic trap work and how can you tell if it is operating properly?

A. The thermostatic trap uses a bellows or diaphragm assembly with a volatile fluid inside. As the fluid inside the element is heated it vaporizes causing an internal pressure to expand the bellows or diaphragms and close the discharge port. The element will close 10 to 30 degrees below the steam temperature to prevent passage of live steam.

The thermostatic trap can fail either closed or open, depending on the design. Failure can occur due to dirt plugging the discharge port or by loss of the internal fill. When the trap fails closed the result will be loss of heat in the unit it serves. When the unit fails open it will pass live steam into the discharge line.

Listening to the trap with an automotive type stethoscope or ultrasound device can test the operation. When the trap is operating properly you will hear it cycle open and closed. When it opens you will hear a wet gurgling sound as condensate flows past the seat. A failed trap blowing live steam will have a hissing sound as live steam blows across the open port.

You can also use an instantaneous type thermometer to check the temperature; the temperature on the trap outlet should be 10 to 30 degrees below the steam temperature at the inlet side. Compare the temperatures at various traps and look for ones that have a higher temperature at the outlet.

Q. How does a F&T (float and thermostatic) trap operate and how can you tell if it is operating?

A. The F&T trap has two separate mechanisms. The float mechanism opens and closes a port for draining condensate. The float assembly modulates to drain condensate equal to the system-condensing rate. The thermostatic assembly vents air from the system into the return line. The thermostatic element is located above the condensate level in the trap. The thermostatic element uses a bellows or diaphragm assembly with a volatile fluid inside. As the fluid inside the element is heated it vaporizes, causing an internal pressure to expand the bellows or diaphragms and close the discharge port. The element will close 10 to 30 degrees below the steam temperature to prevent passage of live steam.

The operation can be tested by listening with an automotive type stethoscope or ultrasound device. When the trap is operating properly you will hear a wet gurgling sound as condensate flows across the seat. A failed trap blowing live steam will have a hissing sound as live steam blows across the open port. The failure can be either the float mechanism or thermostatic element. When the trap is taken apart you can see where the water level was inside the trap housing. If the marking is low in the housing the problem most likely is with the float mechanism.

You can also use an instantaneous type thermometer to check the temperature; the temperature on the trap outlet should be 10 to 30 degrees below the steam temperature at the inlet side.

Some F&T traps have an additional outlet tapping. By installing a ball valve in this additional tapping the trap operation can be monitored. The outlet from the ball test valve should be capped off when the trap is not being tested to prevent accidental opening which may cause live steam to blow.

Q. *How does an air vent work?*

A. Radiator vents and end of main vents operate in a similar manner. The air vent has a float assembly with a pin on top to close the discharge port. The bottom of the float has a metal diaphragm. A volatile fluid is inserted inside the float. When this fluid is heated near saturation temperature it boils and a vapor pressure is created inside the float. The diaphragm expands under the vapor pressure and lifts the float to close the port. The diaphragm is specially constructed to give the vent a snap action to prevent slow closing and spitting. The air vent will also close if condensate gets inside the vent shell.

The most common failure is the vent port getting plugged with dirt or paint. The vent must be located with the port on top for the float to move freely up and down.

Q. *What causes steam vents to spit water?*

A. A properly installed vent should only see air or steam. When vents spit condensate look for a system or installation problem. Main vents installed near an elbow can cause spitting. Main vents should be installed 15 inches ahead of any elbows or bullhead tees; they should be mounted on a pipe nipple 6 to 8 inches above the steam main. Make sure the boiler operating pressure on a gravity return system is properly set. If the boiler pressure exceeds the static head condensate can back up into the steam main. On boiler conversions if the new boiler storage capacity is not large enough for the system time lag, the system will flood at the end of the heating cycle and condensate can get into the vent shell.

On radiators make sure the radiator pitches toward the supply valve. Make sure the supply valve is fully open on a one-pipe radiator. Inspect the supply valve and piping for blockage.

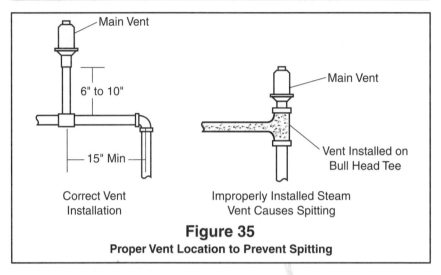

Figure 35
Proper Vent Location to Prevent Spitting

Q. What is a boiler return trap?

A. A boiler return trap was used in some old steam systems to return condensate to the boiler where the available static head in the return line could not permit gravity return.

The boiler return trap has a float connected to open a vent port on low level and open a steam port on high level. The trap water line was higher than the boiler water level but below the dry return line. Condensate could flow into the trap through an inlet check valve by gravity until a high water level was reached. On high level the vent port closes and a port opens to allow boiler pressure into the trap housing. As the trap body pressure equalizes with the boiler pressure condensate flows into the boiler through a second check valve. On low level the steam port closes, the vent opens, and condensate from the return line again flows into the trap housing.

When the old boiler return trap fails it can be replaced with a motor driven condensate transfer pump.

Q. What is boiler horsepower?

A. Boiler horsepower was used to rate steam boilers used to operate a steam engine. It was determined that it took 34.5

lb/hr of steam to operate a 1 horsepower steam engine. Thus you could purchase a 10 horsepower steam engine and a 10 horsepower steam boiler. If the boiler is rated in boiler horsepower multiply the rating by 34.5 to determine the lb/hr steaming rate.

Q. What is a steam riser?

A. A steam riser is the connecting pipe from the steam main to the radiation. Steam risers can be either up-feed or down-feed depending on the system design. Steam risers were designed with a horizontal offset to allow for expansion and contraction in the piping as the system heated.

Q. What is the difference between a condensate transfer pump and a boiler feed pump?

A. A condensate transfer pump is designed for quick transfer of condensate. A level switch on the unit receiver controls the pump. The receiver normally has about 1 minute net storage capacity.

A boiler feed pump is controlled by a level switch on the boiler. The receiver is large enough to store the system time lag. The system time lag is defined as the amount of time required to produce enough steam to fill the heating system. Based on the boiler steaming rate and the time required to fill the system the amount of storage can be determined. This is also the amount of condensate that will return when the steam in the system condenses at the end of the heating cycle. The boiler feed receiver normally has 10 to 20 minutes reserve capacity to feed the boiler.

Q. Can I use a standard globe valve instead of a supply valve?

A. A supply valve has a special design seat to drain all the condensate from the radiator to prevent water hammer. A standard globe valve has a higher seat and condensate can lay in the piping and cause water hammer.

Q. Why do I need an equalizing line on vacuum pumps?

A. The old vacuum heating systems show a $3/4$-inch equalizing line from the vacuum pump to the boiler header. On a zoned system the equalizing line goes to the system side of all zone valves. The function of this equalizer line is to prevent a higher induced vacuum from forming in the header and holding condensate in the system. The $3/4$-inch line includes a check valve that allows airflow from the vacuum pump to the header and prevents steam from the header from going to the vacuum pump. A soft-seated check valve should be used for a tight seal. The check valve is normally set in a in a horizontal pipe slightly below the line. This offset allows condensate to collect at the check valve to protect the check valve elastomer from the steam temperature; the water also provides a tighter seal.

The equalizing line is important to prevent water hammer in the system. The lack of an equalizing line can also contribute to low water conditions in the boiler and the unnecessary addition of boiler make-up water.

Glossary

Accumulator Tank: A storage tank used to collect condensate in a vacuum system. Condensate is lifted from the accumulator tank to the vacuum return line by the vacuum.

Boiler (Steam): A closed vessel in which steam is generated or in which water is heated by fire.

Boiler Header Drip Connection: A piping arrangement from the boiler steam outlet to the boiler return that allows condensate carried with the steam from the boiler to drain back to the boiler return.

Boiler Horsepower: The equivalent evaporation of 34.5 lbs. of water per hour at 212°F to steam at 212°F. This is equal to heat output of 33,475 Btu per hour, which is equal to approximately 140 sq. ft. of steam radiation (EDR).

British Thermal Unit (Btu): The quantity of heat required to raise the temperature of 1 lb. of water 1°F.

Bucket Trap (Inverted): A trap with an open bucket in the inverted position. When air of steam in the bucket has been replaced by condensate the bucket loses its buoyancy and sinks, opening a valve to permit condensate to be pushed into the trap outlet.

Check Valve: A valve that controls water flow in one direction.

Condensate: In steam heating, the water formed by cooling steam in a radiator. The capacity of traps, pumps,

etc., is sometimes expressed in lbs. of condensate they will handle in one hour.

Converter: A piece of equipment for heating water with steam without mixing the two. It may be used for supplying hot water for domestic purposes or for supplying hot water to a hot water heating system.

Cooling Leg: A length of uninsulated pipe through which condensate flows to permit dissipation of heat.

Counter-Flow System: Piping arrangement where the steam and condensate flow in opposite direction in the same pipe.

Deaerator: A boiler feed unit with a heating unit to raise the temperature of the boiler feed unit. .03 Deaerators are normally used to protect low-pressure boilers and .005 Deaerators are used to protect high-pressure boilers. By preheating the boiler feed water, thermal shock to the boiler is reduced and the dissolved oxygen level is lowered to reduce oxygen pitting.

Down Feed System (Steam): A steam heating system in which the supply mains are above the level of the heating units they serve.

Drip Station: The piping arrangement used to install a drip trap. The drip station is designed to direct all condensate in the steam line toward the trap inlet.

Drip Trap: A steam trap used to drain condensate from a steam line. Drip traps are normally installed at the end of a steam line, ahead of any place the steam line rises up and usually every 300 feet along a long run of steam line. The actual trap can be any type of steam trap.

Dry Return (Steam): A return pipe in a steam heating system that carries condensate in the bottom, and the top portion is free to carry air or steam.

Float and Thermostatic Trap: A steam trap with a float element for draining condensate and a thermostatic element for venting air into the return line. A 15-psig trap will have a larger seat and will handle a larger volume of condensate than a 30-psig trap. If a 15-psig rated trap is used on a 30-psig system the higher internal steam pressure against the pin and seat will prevent the trap from opening, thus it will lock shut.

Float Trap: A steam trap, which is operated by a float. The buoyancy of the float in condensate lifts the lever assembly to open the trap seat. Most traps have various pressure ratings determined by the ability of the float to open the trap against the internal steam pressure. A 15-psig trap will have a larger seat and will handle a larger volume of condensate than a 30-psig trap. If a 15-psig rated trap is used on a 30-psig system the higher internal steam pressure against the pin and seat will prevent the trap from opening, thus it will lock shut.

Head: A unit of pressure usually expressed in ft. of water or mil-inch of water. A 23-foot head of water at 70°F is equivalent to approximately 10 psig.

Hot Water Heating System: A heating system in which water is used as the medium by which heat is carried through the pipes from the boiler to the heating units.

Latent Heat of Evaporation: The heat (Btu per hour) necessary to change one pound of water into one pound of steam without changing the temperature. In round numbers this is 960 Btu per pound of water in a low-pressure steam boiler.

Low Water Cut-Off: A low water cut-off is an electrical switch that opens an electrical circuit on low water level. Low water cut-offs can be installed on boilers and boiler feed receivers to protect systems due to low water level.

Low Pressure Steam: Low-pressure steam is normally referred to as steam under 15 psig.

Make-up Water Feeder: Make-up water feeders may be either electrical or mechanical devices to add water on low level. In a steam system they can be mounted on the steam boiler, or on a boiler feed receiver when one is provided in the system.

One-Pipe System (Steam): A steam heating system consisting of a main circuit in which steam and condensate flow in the same pipe. There is also a single pipe connecting the radiation to the main steam circuit that serves as supply and return.

One-Pipe Supply Riser: A pipe which carries steam to a heating unit which also carries the condensate from the heating unit. In an up-feed riser steam travels upward and condensate flows down. In a down-feed riser both steam and condensate flow down.

Parallel-Flow System: Piping arrangement of steam system in which both steam and condensate flow together in the same direction.

Plug Cock: A manual valve used to throttle the flow in a pipe. The plug cock normally has a square head with an indicator to show the plug position and a lock nut to lock to hold the position after it is set to the desired location.

Pre-Heat Unit: A boiler feed unit with a heating unit to raise the temperature of the boiler feed unit. The heater is normally a steam injection assembly and temperature regulator. By preheating the boiler feed water, thermal shock to the boiler is reduced and the dissolved oxygen level is lowered to reduce oxygen pitting.

Pressure Reducing Station: The piping arrangement used to install a pressure-reducing valve. The reducing station normally includes shut-off valves, strainers and a drip trap.

Pressure Reducing Valve: A valve designed to change the steam pressure from high pressure to low pressure in a steam line.

Radiation: The transmission of heat in a straight line through space.

Radiator: A heating unit located within the room to be heated and exposed to view. A radiator transfers heat by radiation to objects and by conduction to the surrounding air, which in turn is circulated by natural convection.

Return Mains: The pipes, which return the heating medium from the heating units to the source of heat supply, normally the boiler.

Sensible Heat: Heat which only increases the temperature of objects as opposed to latent heat.

Square Foot of Heating Surface: Equivalent direct radiation (EDR). By definition, the amount of heating surface which will give off 240 Btu per hour when filled with a heating medium at 215°F and surrounded by air at 70°F. The equivalent square foot of heating surface may have no direct relation to the actual heating surface.

Static Pressure: The pressure which builds as a column of water is developed. A 27-inch column of water will develop 1 psig. Static pressure develops in a vertical return pipe, in a steam system, to offset the boiler operating pressure.

Steam: Water in the vapor phase. The vapor formed when water has been heated to its boiling point.

Steam Heating System: A heating system in which the heating units give up their heat to the room by condensing the steam furnished by a boiler or other source.

Steam Trap: A device for allowing the passage of air and condensate but preventing the passage of live steam.

Thermostatic Trap: A steam trap operated by temperature that closes to prevent the passage of steam and opens to drain condensate.

Vacuum Heating System: A one-pipe or two-pipe steam heating system equipped with a mechanical device to operate the system below atmospheric pressure.

Vapor Heating System: A one-pipe or two-pipe steam heating system equipped with vents that do not permit the re-entry of air at the end of the heating cycle. As the steam in the system condenses, the system operates at sub-atmospheric pressure producing steam at less than 212°F.

About the Author

Joe Mower started his career in the steam industry in 1958 in the engineering and sales departments at Domestic Pump & Manufacturing Company in Shippensburg, Pennsylvania. He conducted field system start-ups and troubleshooting on deaerators and other condensate return pumps.

In 1983 he relocated to the Chicago area, when the company transferred operations there, and taught steam courses in the ITT Training Center. He wrote several of the training manuals in use at the ITT Schoolhouse. Joe later moved to Indianapolis as a product line manager at Hoffman Specialty, working with a wide range of steam products used in residential and commercial heating. When Hoffman Specialty moved to Chicago, he returned to that area.

Joe served 14 years as steam trap standards chairman for the Fluid Controls Institute. He conducted steam training seminars and technical sessions for the American Society of Heating, Refrigeration, and Air Conditioning Engineers (ASHRAE) and other organizations.

After spending 43 years in the steam industry, Joe retired and later returned to work as an outside salesman for Blankin Equipment Company selling heating products in central Pennsylvania.